W9-CTT-471

elevate science

SAVVAS

LEARNING COMPANY

AUTHORS

You're an author!

As you write in this science book, your answers and personal discoveries will be recorded for you to keep, making this book unique to you. That is why you are one of the primary authors of this book.

✏ **In the space below, print your name, school, town, and state. Then write a short autobiography that includes your interests and accomplishments.**

YOUR NAME ....

SCHOOL ....

TOWN, STATE ....

AUTOBIOGRAPHY ....

Your Photo

ISBN-13: 978-1-418-31049-3
ISBN-10:   1-418-31049-2

5 23

Program Authors

ZIPPORAH MILLER, Ed.D.
Coordinator for K-12 Science Programs, Anne Arundel County Public Schools
Dr. Zipporah Miller currently serves as the Senior Manager for Organizational Learning with the Anne Arundel County Public School System. Prior to that she served as the K-12 Coordinator for science in Anne Arundel County. She conducts national training to science stakeholders on the Next Generation Science Standards. Dr. Miller also served as the Associate Executive Director for Professional Development Programs and conferences at the National Science Teachers Association (NSTA) and served as a reviewer during the development of Next Generation Science Standards. Dr. Miller holds a doctoral degree from the University of Maryland College Park, a master's degree in school administration and supervision from Bowie State University and a bachelor's degree from Chadron State College.

MICHAEL J. PADILLA, Ph.D.
Professor Emeritus, Eugene P. Moore School of Education, Clemson University, Clemson, South Carolina
Michael J. Padilla taught science in middle and secondary schools, has more than 30 years of experience educating middle-school science teachers, and served as one of the writers of the 1996 U.S. National Science Education Standards. In recent years Mike has focused on teaching science to English Language Learners. His extensive experience as Principal Investigator on numerous National Science Foundation and U.S. Department of Education grants resulted in more than $35 million in funding to improve science education. He served as president of the National Science Teachers Association, the world's largest science teaching organization, in 2005–6.

MICHAEL E. WYSESSION, Ph.D
Professor of Earth and Planetary Sciences, Washington University, St. Louis, Missouri
Author of more than 100 science and science education publications, Dr. Wysession was awarded the prestigious National Science Foundation Presidential Faculty Fellowship and Packard Foundation Fellowship for his research in geophysics, primarily focused on using seismic tomography to determine the forces driving plate tectonics. Dr. Wysession is also a leader in geoscience literacy and education; he is the chair of the Earth Science Literacy Initiative, the author of several popular video lectures on geology in the *Great Courses* series, and a lead writer of the *Next Generation Science Standards**.

REVIEWERS

Program Consultants

Carol Baker
Science Curriculum

Dr. Carol K. Baker is superintendent for Lyons Elementary K-8 School District in Lyons, Illinois. Prior to this, she was Director of Curriculum for Science and Music in Oak Lawn, Illinois. Before this she taught Physics and Earth Science for 18 years. In the recent past, Dr. Baker also wrote assessment questions for ACT (EXPLORE and PLAN), was elected president of the Illinois Science Teachers Association from 2011–2013, and served as a member of the Museum of Science and Industry (Chicago) advisory board. She is a writer of the Next Generation Science Standards. Dr. Baker received her B.S. in Physics and a science teaching certification. She completed her master's of Educational Administration (K-12) and earned her doctorate in Educational Leadership.

Jim Cummins
ELL

Dr. Cummins's research focuses on literacy development in multilingual schools and the role technology plays in learning across the curriculum. *Elevate Science* incorporates research-based principles for integrating language with the teaching of academic content based on Dr. Cummins's work.

Elfrieda Hiebert
Literacy

Dr. Hiebert, a former primary-school teacher, is President and CEO of TextProject, a non-profit aimed at providing open-access resources for instruction of beginning and struggling readers, She is also a research associate at the University of California Santa Cruz. Her research addresses how fluency, vocabulary, and knowledge can be fostered through appropriate texts, and her contributions have been recognized through awards such as the Oscar Causey Award for Outstanding Contributions to Reading Research (Literacy Research Association, 2015), Research to Practice award (American Educational Research Association, 2013), and the William S. Gray Citation of Merit Award for Outstanding Contributions to Reading Research (International Reading Association, 2008).

Content Reviewers

Alex Blom, Ph.D.
Associate Professor
Department Of Physical Sciences
Alverno College
Milwaukee, Wisconsin

Joy Branlund, Ph.D.
Department of Physical Science
Southwestern Illinois College
Granite City, Illinois

Judy Calhoun
Associate Professor
Physical Sciences
Alverno College
Milwaukee, Wisconsin

Stefan Debbert
Associate Professor of Chemistry
Lawrence University
Appleton, Wisconsin

Diane Doser
Professor
Department of Geological Sciences
University of Texas at El Paso
El Paso, Texas

Rick Duhrkopf, Ph.D.
Department of Biology
Baylor University
Waco, Texas

Jennifer Liang
University of Minnesota Duluth
Duluth, Minnesota

Heather Mernitz, Ph.D.
Associate Professor of Physical Sciences
Alverno College
Milwaukee, Wisconsin

Joseph McCullough, Ph.D.
Cabrillo College
Aptos, California

Katie M. Nemeth, Ph.D.
Assistant Professor
College of Science and Engineering
University of Minnesota Duluth
Duluth, Minnesota

Maik Pertermann
Department of Geology
Western Wyoming Community College
Rock Springs, Wyoming

Scott Rochette
Department of the Earth Sciences
The College at Brockport
 State University of New York
Brockport, New York

David Schuster
Washington University in St Louis
St. Louis, Missouri

Shannon Stevenson
Department of Biology
University of Minnesota Duluth
Duluth, Minnesota

Paul Stoddard, Ph.D.
Department of Geology and
 Environmental Geosciences
Northern Illinois University
DeKalb, Illinois

Nancy Taylor
American Public University
Charles Town, West Virginia

Teacher Reviewers

Rita Armstrong
Los Cerritos Middle School
Thousand Oaks, California

Tyler C. Britt, Ed.S.
Curriculum & Instructional
Practice Coordinator
Raytown Quality Schools
Raytown, Missouri

Holly Bowser
Barstow High School
Barstow, California

David Budai
Coachella Valley Unified School District
Coachella, California

A. Colleen Campos
Grandview High School
Aurora, Colorado

Jodi DeRoos
Mojave River Academy
Colton, California

Colleen Duncan
Moore Middle School
Redlands, California

Nicole Hawke
Westside Elementary
Thermal, California

Margaret Henry
Lebanon Junior High School
Lebanon, Ohio

Ashley Humphrey
Riverside Preparatory Elementary
Oro Grande, California

Adrianne Kilzer
Riverside Preparatory Elementary
Oro Grande, California

Danielle King
Barstow Unified School District
Barstow, California

Kathryn Kooyman
Riverside Preparatory Elementary
Oro Grande, California

Esther Leonard M.Ed. and L.M.T.
Gifted and Talented Implementation Specialist
San Antonio Independent School District
San Antonio, Texas

Diana M. Maiorca, M.Ed.
Los Cerritos Middle School
Thousand Oaks, California

Kevin J. Maser, Ed.D.
H. Frank Carey Jr/Sr High School
Franklin Square, New York

Corey Mayle
Brogden Middle School
Durham, North Carolina

Keith McCarthy
George Washington Middle School
Wayne, New Jersey

Rudolph Patterson
Cobalt Institute of Math and Science
Victorville, California

Yolanda O. Peña
John F. Kennedy Junior High School
West Valley City, Utah

Stacey Phelps
Mojave River Academy
Oro Grande, California

Susan Pierce
Bryn Mawr Elementary
Redlands Unified School District
Redlands, California

Cristina Ramos
Mentone Elementary School
Redlands Unified School District
Mentone, California

Mary Regis
Franklin Elementary School
Redlands, California

Bryna Selig
Gaithersburg Middle School
Gaithersburg, Maryland

Pat (Patricia) Shane, Ph.D.
STEM & ELA Education Consultant
Chapel Hill, North Carolina

Elena Valencia
Coral Mountain Academy
Coachella, California

Janelle Vecchio
Mission Elementary School
Redlands, California

Brittney Wells
Riverside Preparatory Elementary
Oro Grande, California

Kristina Williams
Sequoia Middle School
Newbury Park, California

Safety Reviewers

Douglas Mandt, M.S.
Science Education Consultant
Edgewood, Washington

Juliana Textley, Ph.D.
Author, NSTA books on school science safety
Adjunct Professor
Lesley University
Cambridge, Massachusetts

California Spotlight
Instructional Segment 4

TOPICS 10–12

Gold Mining in California

Anchoring Phenomenon 1

TOPIC 10 Plate Tectonics 8

Investigative Phenomenon Why is it important to analyze and interpret data to provide evidence for past plate motions?

Quest PBL To Hike or Not to Hike 10

 MS-ESS2-2, MS-ESS2-3, MS-ESS3-2, EP&CIb

LESSON 1 Evidence of Plate Motions 12
Literacy Connection Cite Textual Evidence 14
Quest CHECK-IN Patterns in the Cascade Range 20
It's All Connected The Slow Acceptance of
Continental Drift 21

LESSON 2 Plate Tectonics and Earth's Surface 22
Literacy Connection Integrate with Visuals 27
Math Toolbox Reason Quantitatively 28
Quest CHECK-IN Mount Rainier's Threat 31

LESSON 3 Earthquakes and Tsunami Hazards 32
Math Toolbox Analyze Graphs 39
Literacy Connection Evaluate Media 40
Quest CHECK-IN Monitoring a Volcano 42
Engineer It! STEM Designing to Prevent Destruction 43

LESSON 4 Volcanoes and Earth's Surface 44
Literacy Connection Integrate with Visuals 48
Math Toolbox Analyze Proportional Relationships............ 51
Quest CHECK-IN Signs of Eruption? 53

Review and Assess
Evidence-Based Assessment. 54
Quest FINDINGS Reflect on Mount Rainier's Safety 55
Demonstrate Modeling Sea-Floor Spreading 56

HANDS-ON LABS

Connect
Investigate
Demonstrate

TOPIC
11
Distribution of Natural Resources

...........60

Investigative Phenomenon How can you explain the uneven distributions of Earth's natural resources?

 MS-ESS3-1, EP&CIc

LESSON 1 Nonrenewable Energy Resources 62

  Math Toolbox Analyze Relationships 68

  Literacy Connection Cite Textual Evidence 69

  Engineer It! STEM Micro-Hydro Power 73

LESSON 2 Mineral Resources 74

  Literacy Connection Determine Meaning 76

LESSON 3 Water Resources 82

  Math Toolbox Draw Comparative Inferences 84

  Literacy Connection Support Author's Claim 86

  It's All Connected Managing California's Water Resources .. 89

Review and Assess

  Evidence-Based Assessment 90

  Demonstrate To Drill or Not to Drill 92

HANDS-ON LABS

Connect

Investigate

Demonstrate

 TOPIC

12 Human Impacts on the Environment

........96

Investigative Phenomenon What actions can we take to reduce our impact on Earth's systems?

 KICKOFF Trash Backlash 98

MS-ESS3-4, MS-ETS1-4, EP&CIa, EP&CIb, EP&CIc, EP&CIIa, EP&CIIb, EP&CIIc, EP&CIIIc, EP&CIVa, EP&CIVb, EP&CIVc, EP&CVa

LESSON 1 Population Growth and Resource Consumption 100

Math Toolbox Interpret Data 103

Literacy Connection Determine Conclusions 105

Quest CHECK-IN More Trash, Less Space 107

LESSON 2 Air Pollution 108

Literacy Connection Cite Textual Evidence 112

Math Toolbox Analyze Quantitative Relationships 114

Quest CHECK-IN Trash vs. Water 116

Global to Local Reducing Climate Change Together 117

LESSON 3 Impacts on Land 118

Math Toolbox Analyze Proportional Relationships 123

Literacy Connection Cite Textual Evidence 125

Quest CHECK-IN Life of a Landfill 129

LESSON 4 Water Pollution 130

Literacy Connection Draw Evidence 133

Math Toolbox Analyze Proportional Relationships 135

Quest CHECK-IN Reducing Waste 138

Engineer It! STEM From Wastewater to Tap Water 139

Review and Assess

Evidence-Based Assessment 140

Quest FINDINGS Reflect on Trash Backlash 141

Demonstrate Washing Away 142

Case Studies 146

California Spotlight

Gold Mining in California

Conduct an Investigation 151

Communicate a Solution 153

Appendices, Glossary, Index 154

HANDS-ON LABS

Connect

Investigate

Demonstrate

Go to SavvasRealize.com to access your digital course.

Elevate Science combines the best science narrative with a robust online program. Throughout the lessons, digital support is presented at point of use to enhance your learning experience.

Online Resources

Savvas Realize™ is your online science class. This digital-learning environment includes:

- Student eTEXT
- Instructor eTEXT
- Project-Based Learning
- Virtual Labs
- Interactivities
- Videos
- Assessments
- Study Tools
- and more!

Digital Features

 VIDEO

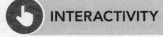 INTERACTIVITY

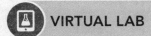 VIRTUAL LAB

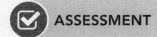 ASSESSMENT

 eTEXT

 APP

Keep an eye out for these **icons**, which indicate the different ways your textbook is enhanced online.

Digital activities are located throughout the narrative to deepen your understanding of scientific concepts.

 INTERACTIVITY

Interpret models of relationships in various ecosystems.

Elevate your thinking!

California Elevate Science takes science to a whole new level and lets you take ownership of your learning. Explore science in the world around you. Investigate how things work. Think critically and solve problems! *California Elevate Science* helps you think like a scientist, so you're ready for a world of discoveries.

Exploring California

California spotlights explore California phenomena. Topic Quests help connect lesson concepts together and reflect 3-dimensional learning.

- Science concepts organized around phenomena
- Topics weave together 3-D learning
- Engineering focused on solving problems and improving designs

Student Discourse

California Elevate Science promotes active discussion, higher order thinking and analysis and prepares you for high school through:

- High-level write-in prompts
- Evidence-based arguments
- Practice in speaking and writing

California Spotlight
Instructional Segment 2

Before the Topics
Identify the Problem

California Flood Management

Phenomenon In February of 2017, workers at the Orov

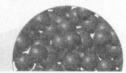

Quest KICKOFF

How can you use solids, liquids, and gases to lift a car?

STEM Phenomenon Auto mechanics often need to go under cars to repair the parts in the under-carriage, such as the shocks and exhaust

Model It

Crystalline and Amorphous Solids
Figure 5 A pat of butter is an amorphous solid. The particles that make up the butter are not arranged in a regular pattern. The sapphire gem stones are crystalline solids. Draw what you think the particles look like in a crystalline solid.

READING CHECK Explain In your own words, explain the main differences between crystalline solids and amorphous solids.

Quest CHECK-IN

In this lesson, you learned what happens to the particles of substances during melting, freezing, evaporation, boiling, condensation, and sublimation. You also thought about how thermal energy plays a role in these changes of state.

Predict Why do you need to take the temperature of the surroundings into consideration when designing a system with materials that can change state?

Academic Vocabulary

In orange juice, bits of pulp are suspended in liquid. Explain what you think *suspended* means.

Build Literacy Skills

By connecting science to other disciplines like:

- Mathematics
- Reading and Writing
- STEM/Engineering

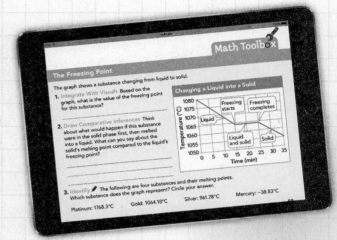

Focus on Inquiry

Case studies put you in the shoes of a scientist to solve real-world mysteries using real data. You will be able to:

- Analyze data
- Formulate claims
- Build evidence-based arguments

Enter the Digital Classroom

Virtual labs, 3-D expeditions, and dynamic videos take science beyond the classroom.

- Open-ended virtual labs
- Google Expeditions and field trips
- NBC Learn videos

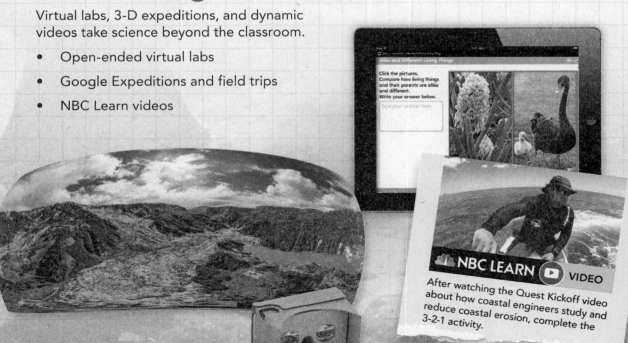

How does human consumption of natural resources affect ecosystems?

Explore It

Look at the picture. What do you observe? What questions do you have about the phenomenon? Write your observations and questions in the space below.

....

....

....

....

....

....

....

....

....

....

....

....

....

....

....

....

....

....

....

....

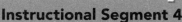
MS-ESS2-2, MS-ESS2-3, MS-ESS3-1, MS-ESS3-3, MS-ESS3-4, EP&CIc, EP&CIIb, EP&CIIIa

Inquiry

- How can the shapes of landforms at the surface help us understand processes that are going on deep within the Earth?
- How does our understanding of geological processes help us locate valuable energy, mineral, and water resources?
- What effect do humans have on the environment?

Topics

10 Plate Tectonics

11 Distribution of Natural Resources

12 Human Impacts on the Environment

Before the Topics
Identify the Problem

Gold Mining in California

Phenomenon On January 24, 1848, a carpenter named James W. Marshall came upon a nugget of gold in Sutter Creek in the Sierra Nevada foothills. News of Marshall's find spread quickly, sparking what would come to be known as the California Gold Rush. The valuable metal has been mined in the state ever since. Riches have been made, but mining has also had serious negative effects on the ecosystems of California.

Following the discovery of gold, thousands of people flocked to the "Gold Country" of California to seek their fortunes. Gold fields were primarily located around Coloma, in the northeastern part of the state, and between Yreka and Shasta, in the northern part of the state.

Geology of a Gold Rush

Gold is a mineral that can be found all over Earth. In most places, it exists only as very small specks mixed in with much larger amounts of rock and other minerals. For this reason, looking for gold in most places is not worth the effort. In some places, however, geological forces concentrate gold in larger amounts and place it closer to the surface. California happens to be one of those places.

Large flecks of gold are visible in this quartz rock.

Earth's crust is broken up into pieces called plates. California sits at the meeting point of the Pacific Plate and the North American Plate. These plates are sliding past each other, with parts of the Pacific Plate slowly sinking under the North American Plate. This interaction is responsible for volcanic activity and the formation of mountain ranges parallel to the coast. As molten rock moves from Earth's interior toward the surface, it picks up particles of minerals and metals, including gold. As the molten rock cools, minerals in it crystalize into veins of rock, called quartz. The deposits of gold remain trapped inside the quartz. Over time, some of these rocks weather and erode. The gold gets carried away by streams and rivers. Other gold deposits remain trapped in rock. California gold miners eventually found ways to remove these deposits.

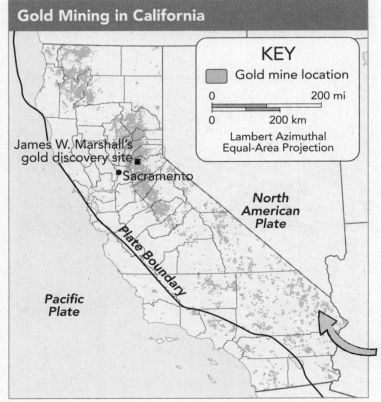

Gold Mining in California

KEY
Gold mine location
0   200 mi
0   200 km
Lambert Azimuthal
Equal-Area Projection

James W. Marshall's gold discovery site
• Sacramento

North American Plate

Plate Boundary

Pacific Plate

Gold was found throughout California, with the greatest concentrations in a few regions.

1. **SEP Use Models** 🖉 On the map, circle two areas where gold mining was most concentrated.

2. **CCC Cause and Effect** Why are there more mining sites in these areas than in other parts of California?

....
....
....
....
....

Early Mining Methods

The earliest California miners mostly found gold by panning for it. They sifted through the sediment in the bottom of rivers, using a pan that was shaped like a pie plate. They then used the running water to help them separate any gold from the rest of the small bits of rock. The water helped to clean away dust from the sediment so miners could see what they had. After rinsing and separating, miners sometimes found a few small nuggets of gold. Often they found nothing. Panning was physically difficult work, and it rarely yielded significant amounts of gold.

To increase efficiency, some miners used sluice boxes to help them sift through more sediment. The sluice box worked using the same principles as panning. River water was poured through the sluice. Gold settled to the bottom and the rest of the sediment was washed away.

These processes left a great deal of environmental damage in their wake. They disturbed riverbeds and stirred up sediment in rivers. As a result, aquatic plants suffered from a lack of sunlight, and so did the organisms in these ecosystems that relied on these plants for food and shelter. However, the impact of these methods on California ecosystems was minimal compared to what miners would later do as gold became more difficult to extract.

These gold nuggets were discovered in a river in California. They have been made smooth by the running water.

Sluicing was a popular method for separating gold from gravel in California.

Hydraulic Mining

Eventually, miners figured out that the source of the gold they were finding in rivers was the steep cliffs of loose gravel along the rivers. To get at this gold, mining companies began to use a system called hydraulic mining, which used high-pressure hoses to shoot water at the cliffs. The gravel broke up and washed away. Then, the gravel and water moved through sluices that separated the gold from other sediments.

Hydraulic mining was an efficient way to mine gold, but it also caused significant damage to California ecosystems. Leftover sediment was dumped into nearby rivers and streams, many of which had already been damaged by people panning for gold. Some rivers became so clogged with sediment that fish could not swim in them anymore. As a result, many water and wetland habitats were gravely harmed or disappeared completely. The buildup of sediment and the resulting floods affected farmers and towns downstream as well. In 1884, after an outcry from farmers and other concerned citizens, the state outlawed the dumping of mining debris in rivers.

Hydraulic mining relied on pressurized water to break up gravel so gold could be separated from it.

Compare and Contrast 🖊
Complete the Venn diagram to compare and contrast hydraulic mining with earlier mining methods.

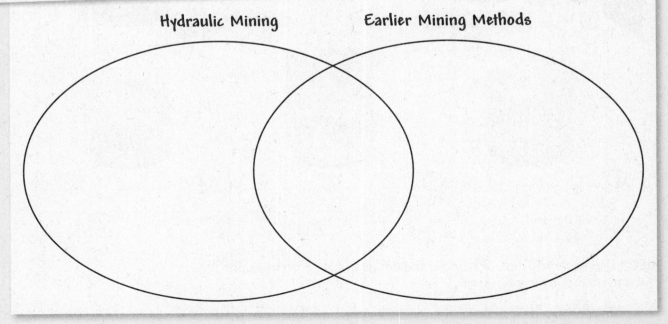

Hydraulic Mining   Earlier Mining Methods

Mercury Contamination

Miners were also eager to remove gold from hard veins of quartz even farther up in the mountains. This type of mining, which is called hard rock mining, was particularly challenging. In these areas, gold was stuck inside solid rock. To get at the gold, miners dynamited the rock and then ground it into a fine powder. Then, they used mercury to help separate the gold from the sediments. It was a groundbreaking feat of engineering. However, mercury is toxic. It causes brain and nerve damage in most living things. Mercury absorbed by plants eventually finds it way into other organisms in an ecosystem. Mercury hasn't been used in mining since the 1960s. Yet, even today, many old mines in California and the waterways near them are not safe to visit because of mercury contamination.

In this segment, you will learn about the theory of plate tectonics and how natural resources are distributed on Earth. You will also learn how human activities, such as mining and farming, affect other living things and ecosystems. As you read the topics, think about the impacts that our use of natural resources has on the environment.

Mining companies relied on a process that used mercury to remove gold from rock.

Gold stuck in rocks

Mercury

① ....

....

② ....

....

....

③ ....

....

④ ....

....

....

⑤ ....

....

....

⑥ ....

SEP Develop Models ✏ Under the images, write a description of what happens at each step.

What questions can you ask to help you make sense of this phenomena?

Plate Tectonics

Investigative Phenomenon
Why is it important to analyze and interpret data to provide evidence for past plate motions?

MS-ESS2-2 Construct an explanation based on evidence for how geoscience processes have changed Earth's surface at varying time and spatial scales.

MS-ESS2-3 Analyze and interpret data on the distribution of fossils and rocks, continental shapes, and seafloor structures to provide evidence of the past plate motions.

MS-ESS3-2 Analyze and interpret data on natural hazards to forecast future catastrophic events and inform the development of technologies to mitigate their effects.

EP&CIb Students should be developing an under-standing that the ecosystem services provided by natural systems are essential to human life and to the functioning of our economies and cultures.

HANDS-ON LAB

uConnect Explore how Earth's continents can be linked together.

How did these chain islands get here?

What questions do you have about the phenomenon?

....
....
....
....
....
....
....
....
....
....
....

Quest PBL

To Hike or Not to Hike

STEM **Figure It Out** Camping and hiking in the mountains are popular pastimes for people all over the world. But are you safe if the mountain is actually an active volcano? It hasn't erupted for thousands of years—but it *could*. Would volcanologists say it is safe to hike? What kinds of data do they collect to predict eruptions? In this problem-based Quest activity, you will determine whether it is safe to take an extended camping and hiking trip on Mount Rainier. Through hands-on labs and digital activities, you'll gather evidence about Rainier's history and look into current research on the mountain's volcanic activity. You will use this information to create a presentation that supports your claim and synthesizes your findings.

👆 **INTERACTIVITY**

To Hike or Not to Hike

🧪 MS-ESS2-2, MS-ESS3-2

📺 NBC LEARN ▶ VIDEO

After watching the Quest Kickoff video, which explains volcanic processes, think about the pros and cons of hiking on Mount Rainier. Record your ideas.

PROS

....

....

....

CONS

....

....

....

Quest CHECK-IN

IN LESSON 1

STEM What is Mount Rainier's history of eruption? Investigate the history of the Cascade Range and draw conclusions about the likelihood of an eruption.

🧪 **HANDS-ON LAB**

Patterns in the Cascade Range

Quest CHECK-IN

IN LESSON 2

How is volcanic activity related to tectonic plate movements? Explore the science behind the connection.

👆 **INTERACTIVITY**

Mount Rainier's Threat

Quest CHECK-IN

IN LESSON 3

What processes cause earthquakes and tsunamis to form? Think about the possible risks from movements of the ground beneath your feet.

👆 **INTERACTIVITY**

Monitoring a Volcano

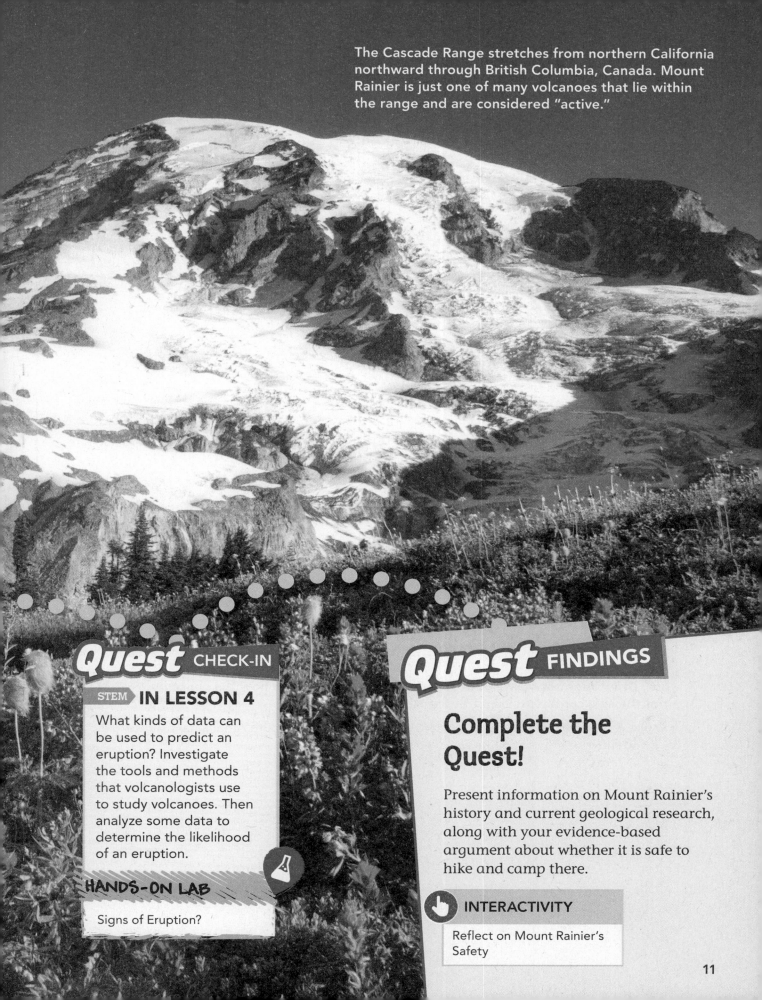

The Cascade Range stretches from northern California northward through British Columbia, Canada. Mount Rainier is just one of many volcanoes that lie within the range and are considered "active."

Quest CHECK-IN

STEM IN LESSON 4

What kinds of data can be used to predict an eruption? Investigate the tools and methods that volcanologists use to study volcanoes. Then analyze some data to determine the likelihood of an eruption.

HANDS-ON LAB

Signs of Eruption?

Quest FINDINGS

Complete the Quest!

Present information on Mount Rainier's history and current geological research, along with your evidence-based argument about whether it is safe to hike and camp there.

INTERACTIVITY

Reflect on Mount Rainier's Safety

① Evidence of Plate Motions

HANDS-ON LAB

uInvestigate Piece Pangaea together.

MS-ESS2-3 Analyze and interpret data on the distribution of fossils and rocks, continental shapes, and seafloor structures to provide evidence of the past plate motions.

Connect It!

✏️ **Draw lines between South America and Africa to show how the contours of the two continents could fit together.**

CCC Stability and Change What might you infer about South America and Africa if you thought the continents were movable objects?

....

Hypothesis of Continental Drift

For many centuries, scientists and map-makers had been curious about why some continents look as though they could fit together like the pieces of a jigsaw puzzle. The continents on the east and west sides of the South Atlantic Ocean, for example, looked like they would fit together perfectly (**Figure 1**). In the mid 1800s, scientists began to gather clues that suggested the slow movement, or drift, of continents. In 1912, German meteorologist Alfred Wegener (VAY guh nur) further developed the **hypothesis** that all of of the continents had once been joined together, and that over time they had moved great distances and spread apart. This hypothesis became known as "continental drift."

In 1915, after gathering evidence that supported the hypothesis, Wegener published *The Origin of Continents and Oceans*. The book connected clues from investigations of land features, types of rock, fossils (traces of organisms preserved in rock), and climate. Evidence at local and global scales led Wegener to map ancient land and water patterns. He made a compelling case for the hypothesis that a supercontinent called Pangaea (pan JEE uh) had broken up into the continents we know today.

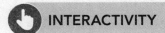

INTERACTIVITY

Try your hand at piecing together puzzles.

Academic Vocabulary

In science, a hypothesis is an idea that can be tested through experimentation or investigation. It is an evidence-based idea that serves as a starting point, whereas a scientific theory is what science produces when a hypothesis has been shown to be true through a broad range of studies. As you read this lesson, highlight or underline the key components of the hypothesis of continental drift.

Pieces of the Puzzle
Figure 1 Scientists wondered whether the continents' coastlines seemed to fit like jigsaw puzzle pieces because they had once been joined together. The light blue areas east of South America and west of Africa are continental shelves. Those areas are parts of the continents, but they are covered by shallow seawater.

Cite Textual Evidence Use your science notebook to organize the evidence that supports the hypothesis of continental drift. Identify a common theme among the different pieces of evidence.

Evidence From Land Features There were other pieces of evidence to support the hypothesis of continental drift. Mountain ranges near those continents' coasts seemed to line up, as though they had been made in the same place and at the same time. Coal deposits, made of the remains of plants that thrived in warm locations millions of years ago, were found on multiple continents and in regions that no longer supported that kind of plant life. The similarity of features found in separate, scattered locations (**Figure 2**) suggested that they hadn't always been separate.

Evidence From Fossils Geologists noticed that evidence from the fossil record supported continental drift. (**Figure 2**). Geologist Edward Suess noted that fossils of *Glossopteris* (glaw SAHP tuh ris), a fernlike plant from 250 million years ago, were found on five continents. This suggested that those landmasses had once been connected, as part of Pangaea. Fossils of animals told a similar story. *Mesosaurus* was a reptile that lived in fresh-water habitats millions of years ago, yet *Mesosaurus* fossils were found in the same types of rock in both South America and Africa.

Evidence for Continental Drift

Figure 2 Study the map key to see how Wegener pieced together similar pieces of evidence from separate sites to support his hypothesis. Then integrate technical information from the text with the version of the information shown in the diagram.

Integrate with Visuals Present-day India is in South Asia, at the northern end of the Indian Ocean. What evidence found in India matches that of other locations?

....

....

....

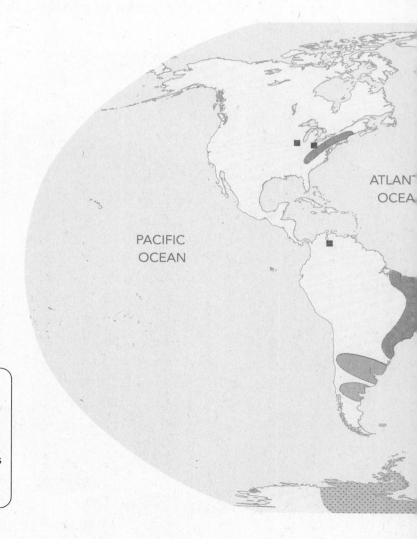

ATLANTIC OCEAN

PACIFIC OCEAN

KEY
- Folded mountains
- Coal beds
- Glacial deposits
- *Glossopteris* fossils
- *Lystrosaurus* fossils
- *Mesosaurus* fossils

Evidence From Climate Wegener, whose own expertise was in the study of weather and climate and not geology, also gathered evidence that showed Earth's continents had experienced different climates than the ones they have today. For example, Spitsbergen, an island in the Arctic Ocean, has fossils of plants that could have survived only in a tropical climate. This doesn't mean that the Arctic Ocean once had a tropical climate. That isn't possible, because the poles do not receive enough sunlight to produce tropical weather or support tropical plants. Instead, this evidence means Spitsbergen used to be near the equator, part of a supercontinent. The supercontinent slowly broke apart, and the island now known as Spitsbergen drifted far to the north over the course of millions of years. Interactions at time scales from the lifetime of a plant to millions of years can be understood in terms of moving continents.

☑ CHECK POINT **Summarize Text** What is the general pattern in the evidence that supports the hypothesis of continental drift?

....

....

HANDS-ON LAB

Investigate Piece Pangaea together.

Reflect Think of some organic item (such as a flower or type of fruit) that you've found in at least two places that are many miles apart. Do the items have a common origin? Why do you think so? What conclusions can you draw from the item's presence in widely different locations?

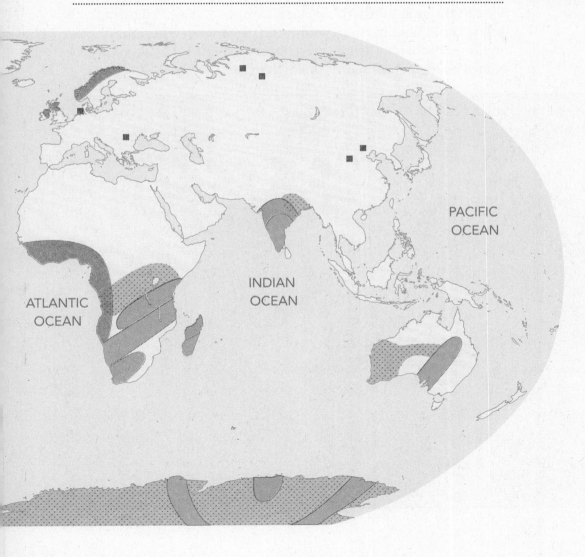

PACIFIC OCEAN

INDIAN OCEAN

ATLANTIC OCEAN

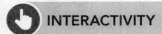
Mid-Ocean Ridges

Figure 3 Mapping of mid-ocean ridges in the mid-1900s provided supporting evidence that Earth's surface was composed of moving plates.

Integrate with Visuals Do any of the mid-ocean ridges appear to extend into continents? Explain which ones.

....

....

....

Mid-Ocean Ridges

The hypothesis of continental drift included evidence from different areas of science, but it had a major flaw. It lacked a good explanation for *how* the continents could have broken up and moved apart. Many scientists rejected the hypothesis for that reason. By the middle of the 1900s, advances in oceanography—the study of Earth's oceans—allowed a mapping of the ocean floor that renewed interest in continental drift. Undersea exploration provided evidence that Earth's surface was composed of moving plates—large pieces of the lithosphere.

By measuring distances from the sea surface to its floor, scientists now had a clear picture of what Earth's surface looked like under the oceans. What surprised many was the presence of long, zipper-like chains of undersea mountains called **mid-ocean ridges**. One such chain, called the Mid-Atlantic Ridge, ran down the middle of the Atlantic Ocean, curving in a pattern that seemed to mirror the contours of the surrounding continental coastlines. Further modeling and mapping of the ocean floor in the 1990s showed that these mid-ocean ridges extend throughout Earth's oceans for about 70,000 kilometers. If you could hold Earth in your hand, the mid-ocean ridges might resemble the seams on a baseball (**Figure 3**). Could these ridges be the actual seams of Earth's crust?

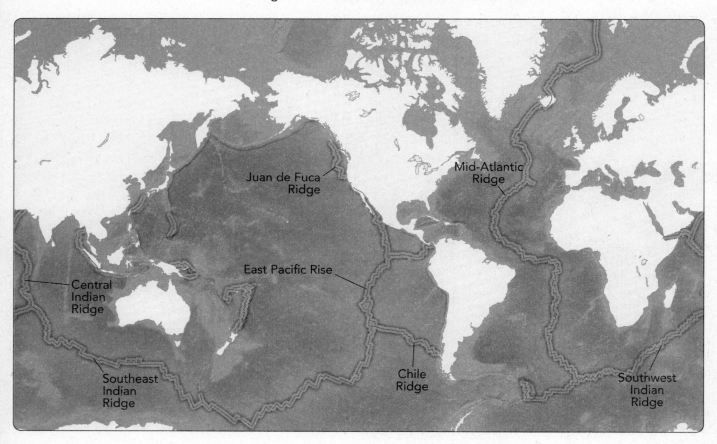

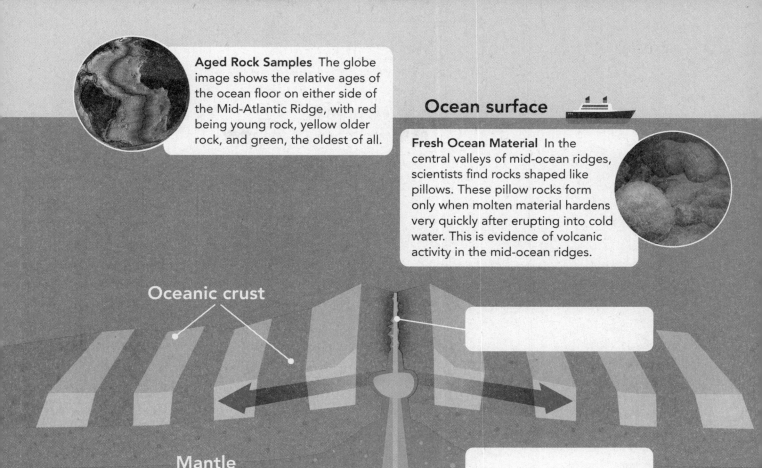

Aged Rock Samples The globe image shows the relative ages of the ocean floor on either side of the Mid-Atlantic Ridge, with red being young rock, yellow older rock, and green, the oldest of all.

Ocean surface

Fresh Ocean Material In the central valleys of mid-ocean ridges, scientists find rocks shaped like pillows. These pillow rocks form only when molten material hardens very quickly after erupting into cold water. This is evidence of volcanic activity in the mid-ocean ridges.

Oceanic crust

Mantle

Sea-Floor Spreading

While ocean-floor mapping was underway, geologists began to gather samples of rock from the ocean floor. They learned that mid-ocean ridges are the sources of new spans of the ocean floor. In a process called **sea-floor spreading**, molten rock flows up through a crack in Earth's crust and hardens into solid strips of new rock on both sides of the crack. The entire floor on either side of the ridge moves away when this occurs, meaning the older strips of rock move farther from the ridge over time. It's like a pair of conveyer belts, with new material appearing at the ridge while older material is carried away. The process goes on at a scale too large to see, so scientists use models. **Figure 4** shows such a model and describes some specific evidence of sea-floor spreading.

✅ CHECK POINT **Cite Textual Evidence** Why was undersea exploration important for developing the theory of plate tectonics?

....

Sea-Floor Spreading
Figure 4 Sea-floor spreading continually adds material to the ocean floor on both sides of the ridge.

SEP Develop Models 🖊
Label the different features that play a role in sea-floor spreading.

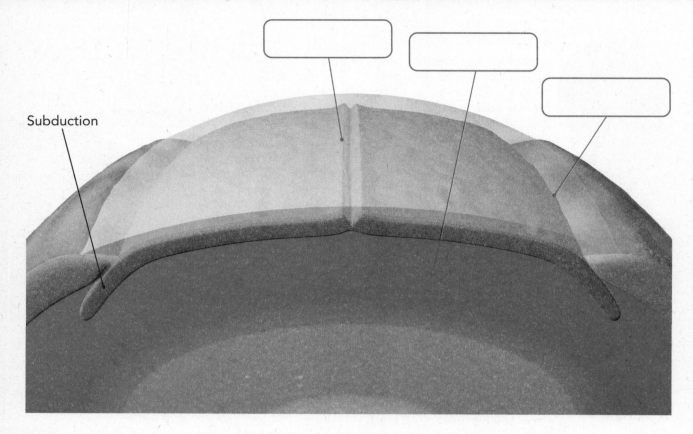

Subduction

Subduction

Figure 5 Oceanic plates, which form through sea-floor spreading, sink back into the mantle at subduction zones.

CCC System Models ✏️
Label the mantle, mid-ocean ridge, and ocean trench.

> ▶ **VIDEO**
>
> Watch what happens at ocean ridges and trenches.

Ocean Trenches

You may be wondering why all of the oceans aren't getting wider, or why Earth as a whole is not expanding, with all of the sea-floor spreading going on. The answer to that is **subduction** (sub DUC shun), or the sinking movement of ocean floor back into the mantle. Subduction occurs where a dense plate of oceanic crust goes under an adjacent section of Earth's crust. This occurs at **ocean trenches**, which are undersea valleys that are the deepest parts of the ocean (**Figure 5**).

The Process of Subduction New oceanic crust is relatively warm. As the rock cools and moves away from a mid-ocean ridge, it gets denser. At some point, the dense slab of oceanic crust may meet another section of ocean floor, or a continent. What happens? Because the oceanic crust is cooler than the mantle underneath, it is denser and will sink into the mantle if given the chance. At an ocean trench, it has that chance, and the oceanic crust will sink under the edge of a continent or a younger, less-dense slab of oceanic crust. The oceanic plate that sinks back into the mantle gets recycled. This process can produce volcanic eruptions at the surface. If the oceanic crust meets continental crust, then a chain of volcanoes will form. If it meets more oceanic crust, then there will likely be a chain of volcanic islands.

Subduction and the Oceans

An ocean basin can have a spreading ridge, subduction zones, or both, depending on its age. The Atlantic Ocean, for example, has the Mid-Atlantic Ridge running down its full length, but no subduction zones. This means that the Atlantic Ocean is still getting wider—by about 2 to 5 centimeters per year. At some point, part of the oceanic plate will begin to sink back into the mantle and a subduction zone will form.

The Pacific Ocean is a more mature ocean basin. While it still has a spreading ridge, the Pacific basin is surrounded by subduction zones. The oceanic crust in the Pacific is being recycled back into the mantle faster than it is being created. This means that the Pacific Ocean basin is getting smaller.

The interactions that have shaped Earth's history will determine its future. Eventually, hundreds of millions of years from now, as Africa collides with Europe, and the Pacific Ocean closes up, a new supercontinent may appear.

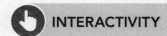
INTERACTIVITY

Learn about the slow and steady movement on Earth.

✓ CHECK POINT **Cite Textual Evidence** What features are evidence of the Pacific Ocean's maturity?

Model It !

Predict North America's Movement

Figure 6 The map shows the layout of some of Earth's landmasses, the mid-ocean ridges where plates are made, and ocean trenches where plates are recycled.

CCC Stability and Change ✏ Draw a line to indicate where you think the west coast of North America will eventually be located.

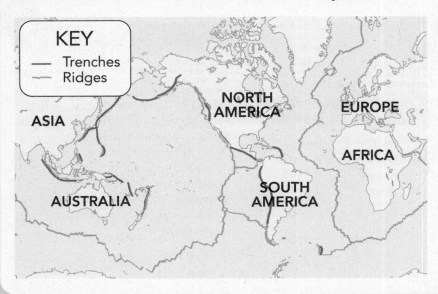

KEY
— Trenches
— Ridges

ASIA
NORTH AMERICA
EUROPE
AFRICA
SOUTH AMERICA
AUSTRALIA

1. **SEP Communicate Information** Describe the hypothesis of continental drift.

....
....
....
....

2. **SEP Analyze Data** How did the study of fossils provide support for the ideas behind the existence of Pangaea?

....
....
....
....
....
....
....
....
....

3. **SEP Interpret Data** How did the discovery of mid-ocean ridges support the hypothesis of continental drift?

....
....
....

4. **CCC Cause and Effect** A large oceanic crust collides with the edge of a continent. What will happen?

....
....
....

5. **Infer** A remotely-operated vehicle is sent to the deepest part of the Mariana Trench. It returns with a sample of rock from the ocean floor. Would this rock be old or young? Explain.

....
....
....
....

Quest CHECK-IN

In this lesson you learned about Wegener's hypothesis of continental drift and how he pieced together evidence from different areas of natural history to support his hypothesis.

Connect to the Nature of Science How can the history of Mount Rainier's eruptions help you decide whether hiking around Mount Rainier is safe?

....
....
....
....

HANDS-ON LAB

Patterns in the Cascade Range

Go online to download the lab worksheet. Analyze data to determine whether there is a pattern to Mount Rainier's eruptions and those of other nearby volcanoes in the Cascade Range of the Pacific Northwest.

The Slow Acceptance of
Continental Drift

"Utter rot," a "fairy tale," and "delirious ravings." These statements are how some scientists in the early 1900s responded to Alfred Wegener's book describing the hypothesis of continental drift.

PANGAEA   EQUATOR

This case demonstrates that scientific thought doesn't always advance neatly or without controversy. Long-held scientific attitudes can be slow to change when new evidence or interpretations are encountered.

The hypothesis of continental drift faced a number of challenges. Though there was evidence to support it, there was not a convincing explanation of how continental drift actually occurred. Scientists who were skeptical of the idea heaped ridicule on Wegener.

In addition, Wegener was a trained meteorologist, but the hypothesis crossed multiple scientific disciplines. Many experts in their respective fields felt threatened because Wegener—viewed as an outsider—challenged their authority and expertise. After his death in 1930, continental drift was virtually ignored.

By the early 1960s, geologists had overcome many of the technological limitations of Wegener's time. They understood more about geological forces, and they were able to explain the mechanism by which the continents moved. The ideas behind continental drift reemerged as the theory of plate tectonics.

Wegener often took research trips to Greenland to study its climate. By taking core samples of ice, climatologists can learn about the climate of the past.

CONNECT TO YOU

Do you think skepticism is an important quality for a scientist to have? Explain why or why not. Discuss your ideas with a partner.

Plate Tectonics and Earth's Surface

uInvestigate Explore different plate interactions.

MS-ESS2-2 Construct an explanation based on evidence for how geoscience processes have changed Earth's surface at varying time and spatial scales.

Connect It!

✎ **Identify where the Himalaya Mountains are and circle them.**

CCC Stability and Change Scientists are measuring Mount Everest to determine whether its height has changed. Why would the Himalayas be getting taller?

....

....

....

The Theory of Plate Tectonics

With observations of many geologists in the 1950s and 1960s, particularly of the features of the ocean floor, the ideas behind continental drift re-emerged as the **theory** of plate tectonics. This theory states that Earth's lithosphere—the crust and upper part of the mantle—is broken up into distinct plates. The plates are puzzle-like pieces that are in slow, constant motion relative to each other due to forces within the mantle. The theory explains the specific patterns of motion among the plates, including the different types of boundaries where they meet and the events and features that occur at their boundaries (**Figure 1**). The term *tectonic* refers to Earth's crust and to the large-scale processes that occur within it.

HANDS-ON LAB

Investigate the role of stress in changing Earth's surface.

Academic Vocabulary

In science, the term *theory* is applied only to ideas that are supported by a vast, diverse array of evidence. How is the term used in everyday life?

....

....

....

....

....

....

Plate Tectonics Give Rise to the Himalayas

Figure 1 The tallest mountains on Earth, K2 and Mount Everest, are part of the Himalayas. When the landmass that is now known as India collided with Asia, these mountains began to form.

Convection Currents

Figure 2 In a pot of boiling water, warmer water rises and cooler water sinks to take its place. This movement creates convection currents in the pot of water.

Convection Drives Plate Motions

The tectonic plates move because they are part of convection currents in the mantle. You may recall that convection is a cyclical movement of fluid driven by temperature differences at the top and bottom, such as cold water sinking from the surface and warm water rising from below (**Figure 2**). Convection occurs in the mantle where rock flows in slow-moving currents. These currents are responsible for moving the continents great distances across Earth's surface, even if they move at speeds too slow to be noticed.

Types of Crust

Plates consist of one or two types of crust. Oceanic crust is the dense type of crust that is found at the bottom of the ocean (**Figure 3**). Some plates, such as the Pacific Plate, consist entirely of oceanic crust. The other type of crust is called continental crust. It is less dense than oceanic crust and is almost always thicker. As a result, the surfaces of continents are above sea level.

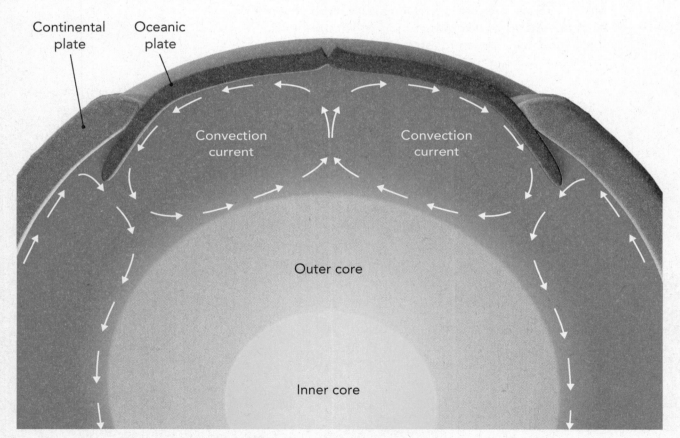

Oceanic and Continental Crust

Figure 3 The very dense crust of the ocean floor is oceanic crust. Crust that is less dense can be thick enough that it's above sea level, which is the case for the continents. The crust that makes up the continents is called continental crust.

Integrate with Visuals ✎ Use the directions in which the convection currents are moving in the figure to draw in arrows indicating the direction of the oceanic plates.

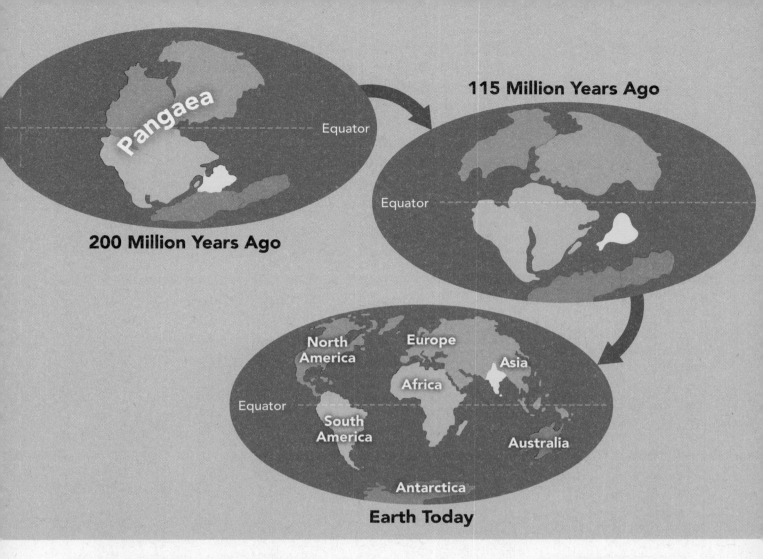

Pangaea

Equator

200 Million Years Ago

115 Million Years Ago

Equator

North America

Europe

Asia

Africa

Equator

South America

Australia

Antarctica

Earth Today

Plate Motions Over Time Scientists use satellites to measure plate motions precisely. The plates move very slowly—about 1 to 10 centimeters per year. The plates that carry North America and Eurasia, move apart at a rate of 1 to 2 centimeters per year, or about as fast as your fingernails grow. The process is slow on a daily scale, but on a scale of billions of years, the plates have moved great distances.

Over time, the movement of Earth's plates has greatly changed the locations of the continents and the size and shape of the ocean basins. Long before Pangaea existed, over billions of years, other supercontinents had formed and split apart. Pangaea itself formed when Earth's plates collided about 350 to 250 million years ago. Then, about 200 million years ago, Pangaea broke up and began to spread apart (**Figure 4**).

☑ CHECK POINT **Draw Conclusions** Suppose the interactions from Earth's history continue into the future. When might the continents of today form a new supercontinent?

200 Million Years of Plate Motions

Figure 4 Since the breakup of Pangaea, it has taken the continents about 200 million years to move to their present locations.

Integrate with Visuals 🖉 Label the landmasses from 115 million years ago with the present-day names of continents, as shown on the "Earth Today" map.

 **INTERACTIVITY**

Compare the relative rates of motion of different plates.

Tectonic Plates and the "Ring of Fire"

The theory of plate tectonics predicts that earthquakes and volcanoes should occur at plate boundaries, and that some landforms, such as mountain ranges, should mark the plate boundaries. For example, many volcanic eruptions and earthquakes occur at the edges of the Pacific Plate (**Figure 5**), which lies under the Pacific Ocean.

Model It!

Ring of Fire

Figure 5 Because the region around the Pacific Ocean is prone to volcanic activity and earthquakes, it is known as the "Ring of Fire."

1. Claim Why do so many volcanoes seem to occur on coastlines of the Pacific Ocean?

....

....

....

....

....

....

▲ Volcanoes

2. Evidence ✎ According to the theory of plate tectonics, how do the locations of volcanoes compare with plate boundaries? On **Figure 5,** draw the edges of the different plates, including the Pacific Plate. Use **Figure 6** to help you.

3. Reasoning Describe how the symbols on the map guided your markup of the map.

....

....

Plate Map

Figure 6 Scientists have identified the different tectonic plates, many of which are named for the continents they carry. The boundaries are either convergent, divergent, or transform. Relative plate movements at some of the boundaries are indicated with red arrows.

SEP Develop Models ✏️ Using the map key as a reference, add the arrows that are missing in the circles provided.

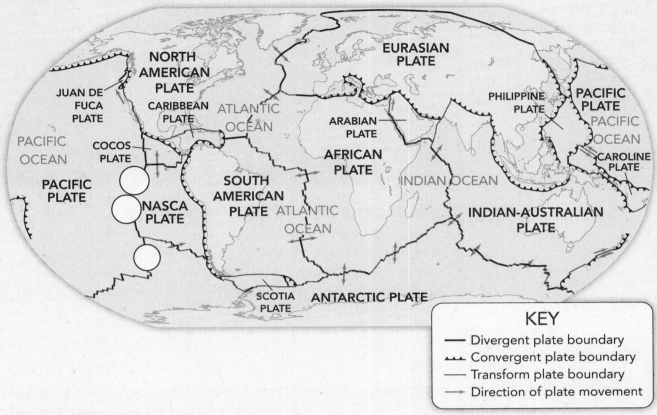

KEY
— Divergent plate boundary
▲▲▲ Convergent plate boundary
— Transform plate boundary
→ Direction of plate movement

Plate Boundaries

Earth's plates meet and interact at boundaries. Along each boundary, plates move in one of three ways. Plates move apart, or diverge, from each other at a **divergent boundary** (dy VUR junt). Plates come together, or converge, at a **convergent boundary** (kun VER junt). Plates slip past each other along a **transform boundary**. The interactions of plates at boundaries produce great changes on land and on the ocean floor. These changes include the formation of volcanoes, mountain ranges, and deep-ocean trenches. Earthquakes and the triggering of tsunamis are also more common at or near plate boundaries. **Figure 6** depicts the major tectonic plates and the types of boundaries between them.

✅ CHECK POINT **Integrate with Visuals** Which of the plates from the map would be a good starting point for a diagram that summarizes the different boundaries? Explain.

....

....

Literacy Connection

Integrate with Visuals
In your science notebook, draw sketches of the different interactions at plate boundaries. Work toward a visual presentation that summarizes the plate boundaries in a single diagram.

👆 **INTERACTIVITY**

Explore surface features associated with plate movement at different locations around the world.

VIDEO

Learn about the tectonic plate boundary types.

Salton Trough

Figure 7 The Salton Sea and the Imperial Valley are in the Salton Trough, a rift valley that crosses the border between California and Mexico.

Divergent Boundaries Mid-ocean ridges and rift valleys are features of divergent boundaries. In some locations, a mid-ocean ridge releases so much molten material that a volcanic island forms. Iceland is an example of this. Iceland contains volcanoes as well as rift valleys that people can walk or even swim through.

Math Toolbox

Rates of Plate Movement

Earth scientists measure plate movement by using the Global Positioning System (GPS) of satellites. Receivers anchored in Earth's surface receive signals from satellites and calculate their positions using the time it takes for signals to be received. Patterns in the rate of change in those signals show the operation of the natural system of plate movement.

1. **Reason Quantitatively** GPS readings suggest that the Mid-Atlantic Ridge spreads about 2.5 cm per year. How fast is the North American Plate moving away from the ridge? Explain your answer.

   ....

   ....

   ....

   ....

   ....

   ....

2. **SEP Use Mathematics** The Pacific Plate moves to the northwest at an average rate of 10 cm per year. Hawaii is in the middle of the Pacific Plate, 6,600 kilometers southeast of Japan, which is on the edge of several adjacent plates. If the Pacific Plate continues to move at the same rate and in the same direction, when will Hawaii collide with Japan? Using the variable t for time, write and solve an equation.

   ....

   ....

   ....

   ....

Convergent Boundaries A boundary where two plates collide, or move toward each other, is called a convergent boundary. If two continents collide, then a mountain range is pushed up, or uplifted. This is how the Himalayas formed, and they are still being uplifted. What is now India used to be a separate continent that broke away from Antarctica and headed north. It began colliding with Asia more than 60 million years ago, and the edges of the two plates folded like the hoods of two cars in a head-on collision (**Figure 8**). Mount Everest and the rest of the Himalayas are the result.

If one or both plates are oceanic, then subduction occurs. The ocean plate always subducts if it collides with a continent. If two oceanic plates collide, the older, colder, and denser plate usually subducts beneath the younger plate, with an ocean trench marking the plate boundary. As a subducting plate sinks back into the mantle, water that was in the ocean crust rises into the overlying mantle, lowering its melting point. Magma forms and rises up through the overlying plate, producing volcanoes. On land, this results in the formation of volcanic mountains. Mountains can also form as ocean seafloor sediments are scraped onto the edge of the overlying plate, forming a large wedge of rock.

Under the sea, subduction produces undersea volcanoes, also known as seamounts. If they grow tall enough, these volcanoes form a volcanic island chain. This is why there are often chains of volcanic islands where convergent boundaries exist in the ocean.

HANDS-ON LAB

и**Investigate** Explore different plate interactions.

Collision at a Convergent Boundary
Figure 8 When two continental plates collide, their collision can have a crumpling effect on the crust that produces tall mountains, just as for two cars in a head-on collision. If one plate is denser, such as a plate of oceanic crust, that denser plate will dive under the other. This can also produce mountains as the overlying plate edge is uplifted.

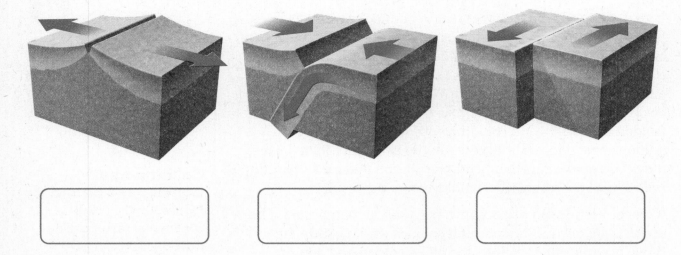

[ ]   [ ]   [ ]

Types of Plate Boundaries

Figure 9 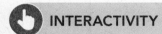 The three types of plate boundaries are modeled here. Label each illustration with the term that describes the boundary.

👆 **INTERACTIVITY**

Investigate how stress is built up and released at faults.

Transform Boundaries Plates slide past each other at a transform boundary. Earthquakes occur here on faults called transform faults. Bending across a fault occurs when the two sides remain locked together. When enough stress builds up, the fault ruptures and an earthquake occurs. This is what causes earthquakes along transform faults such as the San Andreas Fault in California. In some cases a surface feature (such as a stream or road) that crossed a fault is visibly offset after a major slippage of the plates. Depending on how the plate edges match up, a vertical offset can exist across the fault.

Transform faults also form on the ocean floor. They cross mid-ocean ridges at right angles to form fracture zones. The result is the stepped shape of the mid-ocean ridges seen in **Figure 6**.

Keep in mind that the tectonic plates of Earth's lithosphere are three-dimensional objects that are moving around a sphere. The shapes of the plates are irregular. This means every plate has some mixture of the different types of boundaries, and at some point the boundaries may change as the plates shrink, grow, collide, slip past each other, subduct, and so on. Interactions among tectonic plates continue to reshape Earth's surface features.

✓ CHECK POINT **Cite Textual Evidence** What happens at divergent, convergent, and transform boundaries?

....

....

....

☑ LESSON 2 Check

1. **Compare and Contrast** At what type of plate boundary would you find a rift valley that is growing wider?

....

2. **SEP Interpret Data** Describe what is going on in this diagram.

....

....

....

....

....

....

....

3. **CCC Cause and Effect** What other surface feature that is not shown in the diagram could be produced as a result of the process shown?

....

4. **SEP Use Mathematics** It takes 100,000 years for a plate to move about 2 kilometers. What is that plate's rate of motion in centimeters per year? Write and solve an equation, using the variable *s* for speed.

....

....

5. **Connect to Nature of Science** What does the theory of plate tectonics have that Wegener's hypothesis of continental drift did not have?

....

....

....

....

....

....

....

Quest CHECK-IN

In this lesson, you learned about the specific mechanisms by which plates move and how interactions of tectonic plates affect Earth's surface.

SEP Construct Explanations What's the connection between Mount Rainier and the plate boundaries along the coast of the Pacific Northwest?

....

....

....

....

👆 INTERACTIVITY

Mount Rainier's Threat

Go online to learn how Mount Rainier and other volcanic mountains in the Cascade Range formed as a result of geologic activity at tectonic plate boundaries.

③ Earthquakes and Tsunami Hazards

HANDS-ON LAB

иInvestigate
Analyze data and interpret patterns to predict future earthquakes.

MS-ESS2-2 Construct an explanation based on evidence for how geoscience processes have changed Earth's surface at varying time and spatial scales.

MS-ESS3-2 Analyze and interpret data on natural hazards to forecast future catastrophic events.

Connect It!

✏️ **Circle the evidence that an earthquake occurred.**

CCC Cause and Effect How do you think an earthquake caused this damage?

_____

_____

_____

Stress and Earth's Crust

The movement of Earth's massive tectonic plates generates tremendous force. This force can bend and break the rock of Earth's crust. The force that acts on rock to change its shape or volume is called **stress**. There are three kinds of stress. **Tension** pulls on Earth's crust, stretching the rock to make it thinner, especially at the point halfway between the two pulling forces. **Compression** squeezes rock until it bends or breaks. When compression occurs at a large scale, rock can be folded into mountains. **Shearing** occurs when rock is being pushed in two opposite directions, to the point that it bends or breaks. These types of stress can produce both folds and faults. Movement of Earth's crust around faults can produce destructive earthquakes **(Figure 1)** which are internal processes, and, in some cases, tsunamis, which are surface processes.

Make Meaning As you go through the lesson, keep notes in your science notebook about how the physical stresses described here are involved in processes that produce earthquakes and tsunamis.

Earthquake Damage
Figure 1 In 1989, this two-level freeway in Oakland, California, was damaged by the Loma Prieta earthquake.

Death Valley
Figure 2 Tension can result in peaks around a sunken valley, such as Death Valley, in California.

Types of Faults
Figure 3 ✏ **SEP Develop Models** The three types of faults are shown here. Complete diagrams A and B by labeling the hanging walls and footwalls. In Diagram C, draw arrows to indicate the direction of shearing force and the movement along the fault.

Normal Fault
A **fault** is a break in the rock of Earth's crust or mantle. Most faults occur along plate boundaries, where stress of one or more types is deforming the rock, leading to changes at Earth's surface (**Figure 2**). The two sides of a fault are referred to as walls. The wall with rock that is above the fault is called the hanging wall, and the wall that is below the fault is called the footwall. In a normal fault, the hanging wall slips down relative to the footwall (**Figure 3A**). This usually occurs at a divergent plate boundary, where tension is pulling the plates away from each other. In a normal fault, a slab of crust that falls away becomes a valley while the adjacent slab becomes mountains.

Reverse Fault
Compression can produce a reverse fault, in which the hanging wall slides up and over the footwall (**Figure 3B**). The northern Rocky Mountains were gradually lifted by the action at several reverse faults. Reverse faults are common at convergent boundaries.

Strike-Slip Fault
California's San Andreas Fault is a product of shearing. Walls of rock grind past each other in opposite directions, making a strike-slip fault (**Figure 3C**). Transform boundaries are home to strike-slip faults.

✅ **CHECK POINT** **Determine Central Ideas** Pair each fault type with the type of stress that produces it.

....

....

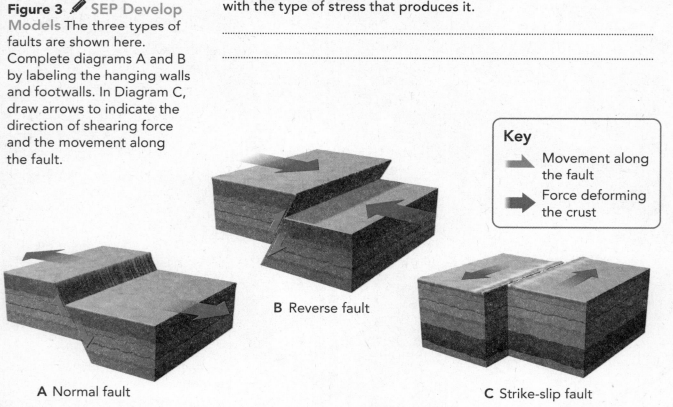

Key
➡ Movement along the fault
➡ Force deforming the crust

A Normal fault

B Reverse fault

C Strike-slip fault

Valleys and Mountains

Figure 4 As tension pulls rock apart along normal faults, some blocks fall, leaving others elevated. Over time, the resulting mountains weather.

Rift valley

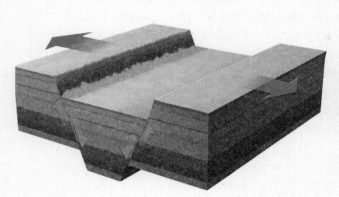

Fault-block mountains

Key

➡ Movement along the fault

➡ Force deforming the crust

New Landforms From Plate Movement

Over millions of years, the forces of plate movement can change a flat plain into folded mountains, fault-block mountains, and other dramatic features of Earth's surface.

Tension and Normal Faults To see how tension and normal faults produce mountains, you need to think on a larger scale and look at a series of at least two normal faults. Where two plates move away from each other, tension forms numerous faults that run parallel to each other over a wide area. A wedge of rock that has hanging walls at both faults drops down to form a rift valley as tension pulls the adjacent footwalls away (**Figure 4**). A wedge of rock that has footwalls at both faults rises up as tension pulls the adjacent footwalls away. Mountains built this way are called *fault-block mountains.*

Folding Compression within a plate causes the crust to deform without breaking. Folds are bends in rock that form when compression shortens and thickens Earth's crust. Folds may be centimeters across or they may span many kilometers. The folds are often most visible and obvious when the rock is layered. When folding occurs on a large **scale,** folds that bend upward become mountains and folds that bend downward become valleys.

Academic Vocabulary

The processes of plate tectonics occur at different scales of time and space. List some different terms that are used to describe distance and time at vastly different scales.

....

....

....

35

Folded Rock

Figure 5 Formations near Palmdale, California, reveal distinct folding patterns.

Anticlines and Synclines

A fold in rock that bends upward into an arch is called an anticline (AN tih klyn). This may resemble the crest of a wave, as seen in **Figure 5**. Weathering and erosion have shaped many large-scale anticlines into mountains. The height of an anticline is exaggerated by the valley-like syncline (SIN klyn), which is a fold that bends downward. This is similar to the trough of a wave. Like a series of fault-block mountains, a series of folded mountains is often marked by valleys between rows of mountains. Viewed at a large scale, a wide area of compressed crust may have mountains and valleys made of anticlines and synclines (**Figure 6**), while the large-scale folds may themselves contain their own anticlines and synclines.

✓ CHECK POINT **Summarize Text** Describe how both compression and tension can create mountains and valleys.

....

....

....

....

Anticlines and Synclines as Mountains and Valleys

Figure 6 ✏ Label the anticlines and synclines in the diagram.

SEP **Evaluate Information** How does this figure oversimplify how compression produces folds in Earth's crust?

....

....

....

Earthquakes

Some plate interactions are gradual, quiet, and almost imperceptible. Others can be sudden, violent, loud, and destructive. At some faults, the plates may grind to a halt and remain stuck in place for years. Stress builds up until the plates lurch into motion, releasing a great amount of energy. The shaking that results from this plate movement is an **earthquake**. Some of the energy released in an earthquake is in the form of seismic waves.

HANDS-ON LAB

Investigate Analyze data and interpret patterns to predict future earthquakes.

Seismic Waves Similar to sound waves, seismic waves are vibrations that travel through Earth carrying energy released by various processes, such as earthquakes, ocean storms, and volcanic eruptions. There are three types of seismic waves, as shown in **Figure 7.** The waves begin at the earthquake's focus, where rock that was under stress begins to break or move. Waves strike most quickly and with the most energy at the point on Earth's surface directly above the earthquake's focus, called the epicenter. But seismic waves also move in all directions, through and across Earth's interior and surface. When seismic waves pass from one material to another, they can change speeds and directions.

P and S Waves

Figure 7 SEP Develop Models The motion of particles in Earth's surface is shown for P waves and S waves. Draw the particle motion for the surface waves.

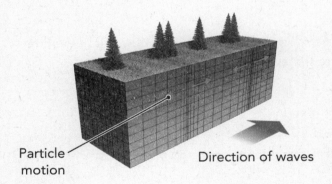

Particle motion — Direction of waves

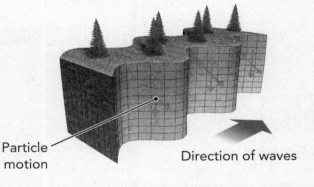

Particle motion — Direction of waves

P waves, short for primary waves, travel the fastest. They are the first to arrive at a location on Earth's surface. P waves compress and expand the ground.

S waves, short for secondary waves, travel more slowly so they arrive after P waves. S waves can move the ground side to side or up and down.

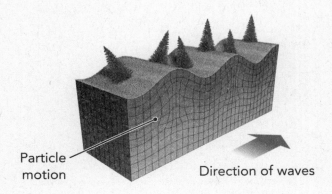

Particle motion — Direction of waves

Surface waves can form when P waves and S waves reach Earth's surface. The result can be a kind of rolling motion, like ocean waves, where particles move in a pattern that is almost circular. Surface waves damage structures on the surface.

Seismogram

Figure 8 The surface waves that travel along Earth's surface usually have the largest amplitudes and therefore cause the most damage.

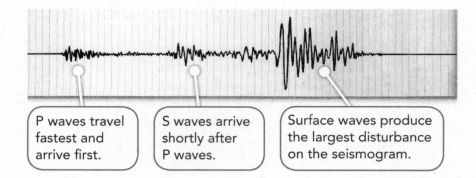

P waves travel fastest and arrive first.

S waves arrive shortly after P waves.

Surface waves produce the largest disturbance on the seismogram.

INTERACTIVITY

Analyze seismic waves to locate an earthquake.

Seismographs

Seismic waves produced by earthquakes are measured by a device called a seismograph, or seismometer. This device converts the energy in the different waves to a visual called a seismogram **(Figure 8)**. The seismogram shows the timing of the different seismic waves, with the relatively gentle P and S waves arriving first, followed by surface waves with larger amplitudes. The amplitudes, or heights, of the waves on a seismogram are used to quantify the size of the earthquake.

When an earthquake occurs, geologists use data from seismograph stations in different locations to pinpoint the earthquake's epicenter **(Figure 9)**. Locating the epicenter helps geologists to identify areas where earthquakes may occur in the future.

✓ CHECK POINT **Determine Central Ideas** Why is it helpful for geologists to locate the epicenters of earthquakes?

....

....

Model It

Triangulation

Figure 9 If you have data from three seismograph stations, you can find the precise location of an earthquake's epicenter. The center of each circle is the location of a station. The radius of each circle is the distance from the epicenter. The point where the three circles cross is the location of the epicenter.

SEP Analyze Data

✏ Draw an X on the map to indicate the epicenter of the earthquake.

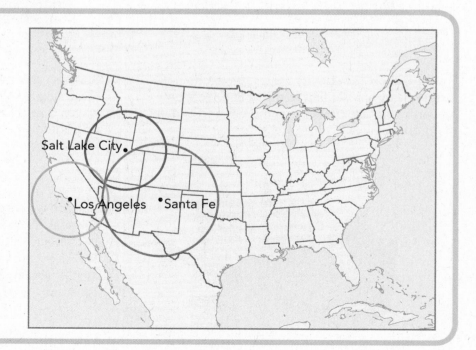

Math Toolbox

Finding an Epicenter

Geologists are trying to locate the epicenter of an earthquake. The data table below shows the arrival times of seismic waves at three different stations across Earth's surface. Use the graph to answer the questions.

Station	P Wave Arrival Time	S Wave Arrival Time	Distance from Epicenter (km)
A	4 min 6 s	7 min 25 s	
B	6 min 58 s	12 min 36 s	
C	9 min 21 s	16 min 56 s	

1. **Analyze Graphs** 🖉 Use the graph to determine the distance of each station from the epicenter. Record the distance in the table.

2. **SEP Interpret Data** If another station were 5,000 km from the epicenter of the earthquake, about how long after the start of the earthquake would the S waves have arrived at this station?

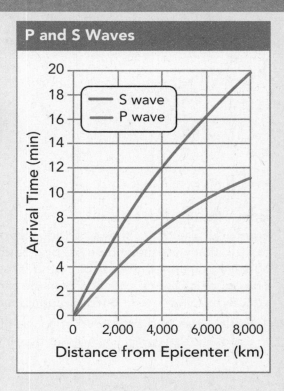

P and S Waves

(Graph: Arrival Time (min) vs Distance from Epicenter (km), showing S wave and P wave curves)

Magnitude An earthquake's **magnitude** is a single number that geologists use to assign to an earthquake based on the earthquake's size. The size of an earthquake is usually measured using the moment magnitude scale, which is a measure of the energy released. Each whole-number increase in this scale represents a roughly 32-fold increase in energy. So, the seismic waves of a magnitude-9 earthquake are 10 times larger than for a magnitude-8 earthquake. The energy released, however, is 32 times greater **(Figure 10)**. To minimize damage from large earthquakes, engineers design buildings with specialized features. Tension ties, base isolators, cross braces, and dampers are used in construction to absorb and scatter earthquake energy or support the building structure.

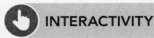

INTERACTIVITY

Explore technologies that help make buildings earthquake resistant.

Magnitude	Location	Date
9.2	Sumatra	2004
9.0	Japan	2011
7.9	China	2008
7.9	Nepal	2015
7.0	Haiti	2010

Earthquake Magnitude

Figure 10 The table shows the moment magnitudes of some large earthquakes.

CCC Scale, Proportion, and Quantity How much more energy was released by the earthquake in China than by the one in Haiti?

39

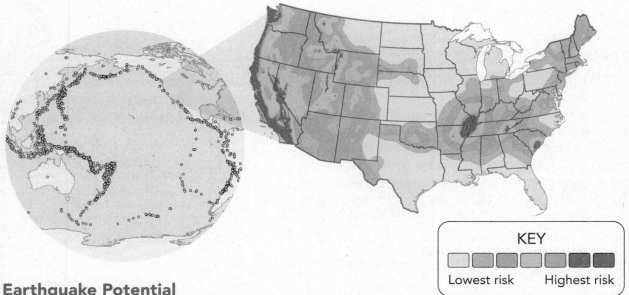

Earthquake Potential

Figure 11 The globe shows earthquakes occurring from 2007 to 2017 that were magnitude 6.0 or greater. The U.S. Geological Survey has mapped the risk of earthquakes in the United States. The risk of injury and property damage can be greatly reduced if structures follow newer building codes, such as those in California.

KEY

Lowest risk   Highest risk

1. **CCC Cause and Effect** What do you think accounts for the higher risk of earthquakes in Los Angeles than in the middle of the U.S.?

....

....

2. **Connect to Society** What societal need would wider use of technology for forecasting earthquakes address?

....

Earthquake Risks and Tsunamis

The "Ring of Fire" around the Pacific Ocean is where many of the world's earthquakes occur. There are many plate boundaries around the Pacific, including convergent and transform boundaries where stress builds up. Because the west coast of the United States, including Alaska, is on the edge of several boundaries, the western states have a much higher risk of experiencing an earthquake than other regions of the United States, as shown in **Figure 11**. Earthquakes themselves can cause tremendous damage, but if they occur near or below the ocean floor, they can produce another type of disaster.

Ocean Floor Uplift
When an area of Earth's crust moves during an earthquake, it forces anything above it to move as well. For example, an area of off-shore ocean floor that has been stressed for years at a convergent plate boundary can suddenly pop up, thrusting up the ocean water above it. Depending on how the water is moved, a tsunami may form.

A **tsunami** is a wave or series of waves produced by an earthquake or landslide. Unlike typical ocean waves formed by the wind, tsunami waves can involve the entire water column—every drop between the surface and the ocean floor. That means they can carry tremendous energy and can be highly destructive **(Figure 12)**. Engineers have developed technologies that record seismic data and sea level changes in the deep ocean, such as tsunami detection buoys, are used in tsunami warning systems to minimize damage and loss of life. If there is a tsunami threat, alerts can be sent via television and radio stations, and some mobile devices. Warning siren systems can also transmit alerts by using different sounds to indicate a tsunami threat, the need to evacuate, or if the threat has passed.

Landslides

Ocean floor uplift is one cause of tsunamis. Landslides are another. In both cases, some kind of displacement of water occurs, setting the tsunami in motion. In 1958, an earthquake triggered a landslide on a mountainside on the shore of Lituya Bay, Alaska. About 30 million cubic meters of rock tumbled into the water at one end of the bay, producing a tsunami that swept across the bay and splashed as high as 524 meters up along the steep shoreline **(Figure 13)**.

✓ CHECK POINT **Cite Textual Evidence** How can an earthquake or landslide produce a tsunami?

....

....

....

A Wall of Water
Figure 12 A tsunami does not always look like a wave. In some cases it is just a sudden, massive rise in sea level, which simply floods low-lying areas.

Tsunami Hazards
Figure 13 The site of the rockslide that produced the tsunami in Lituya Bay is marked by the circle.

SEP Cite Evidence ✏
Draw lines to indicate where the water splashed up and tore away plants and sediment from the bay's shore.

MS-ESS2-2, MS-ESS3-2

1. Identify Which type of stress on Earth's crust can make a slab of rock shorter and thicker?

....

2. SEP Construct Explanations How do mountains and valleys form through folding?

....

....

....

....

....

....

3. Explain Phenomena You hear about a magnitude 8.0 earthquake on the news. Someone says "That doesn't sound too bad. An 8.0 is just one more than the 7.0 we had here last year." Explain why that's not the right way to think about the moment magnitude scale.

....

....

....

....

4. SEP Design Solutions What technologies have engineers developed to reduce the effects of a natural hazard?

....

....

....

....

....

5. CCC Stability and Change Describe the role that stress plays in the production of earthquakes and tsunamis.

....

....

....

....

....

....

....

....

....

....

Quest CHECK-IN

In this lesson, you learned about the connection between plate tectonics and features and events at Earth's surface, including mountains and earthquakes.

Evaluate How can monitoring Earth for seismic activity near plate boundaries be useful in monitoring volcanoes?

....

....

....

....

....

INTERACTIVITY

Monitoring a Volcano

Go online to practice several data collection and analysis techniques to monitor a volcano and predict an eruption.

DESIGNING TO PREVENT
Destruction

▶ **VIDEO**

Watch how underwater earthquakes displace water.

How do you design a building that can withstand the forceful waves of a tsunami? You engineer it!

The Challenge: To construct tsunami-safe buildings.

Phenomenon A seafloor earthquake can displace water above it, causing a tsunami to form. When the tsunami reaches land, giant waves cause widespread destruction.

Because parts of the United States are at risk for tsunamis, U.S. engineers have developed new building standards to save lives and mitigate the damage. They studied new design concepts. Strong columns enable buildings to stand, even when battered by tons of water and debris. Exits on upper floors allow people to get out when lower floors are flooded.

To develop standards, engineers visited Japan, where an earthquake and tsunami in 2011 caused terrible losses of life and property. The engineers also used wave research to model tsunamis and their impact on buildings.

These engineers hope that hospitals, schools, and police stations, if built to the new standards, can then provide shelter for people fleeing danger.

Though much smaller than the one that struck Japan in 2011, a 1964 tsunami devastated Crescent City, California, shown above.

It is a challenge to design and engineer structures that can withstand the force of a tsunami. Under new standards, schools would be built to withstand the force of water and debris. This increases the cost of construction, but the improved safety far outweighs the added cost.

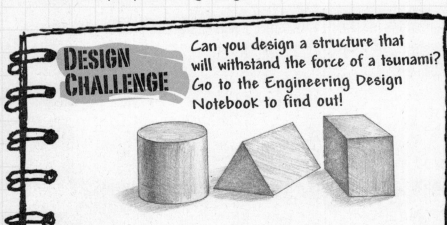

DESIGN CHALLENGE Can you design a structure that will withstand the force of a tsunami? Go to the Engineering Design Notebook to find out!

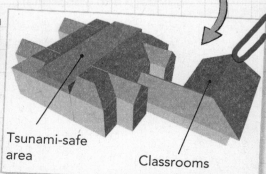

Tsunami-safe area

Classrooms

LESSON 4

Volcanoes and Earth's Surface

HANDS-ON LAB

uInvestigate Explore moving volcanoes.

MS-ESS2-2 Construct an explanation based on evidence for how geoscience processes have changed Earth's surface at varying time and spatial scales.

MS-ESS3-2 Analyze and interpret data on natural hazards to forecast future catastrophic events. (Also **EP&CIb**)

Connect It!

✏ **Circle and label effects that the volcano in the photo is having on Earth's surface and atmosphere.**

CCC Systems List the effects that you identified in the photo, and categorize them by the Earth system that is affected—hydrosphere, atmosphere, geosphere, biosphere.

....

....

....

....

Volcanoes

While active volcanoes are found in a relatively small number of states in the United States, they have a profound effect on Earth's surface—especially at plate boundaries. Volcanoes add new material to Earth's surface, release gases into the atmosphere, build new islands, shape habitats for organisms and enrich soil with volcanic ash. A **volcano** is a structure that forms in Earth's crust when molten material, or magma, reaches Earth's surface. This can occur on land or on the ocean floor. **Magma** is a molten mixture of rock-forming substances, gases, and water from the mantle. Once magma reaches the surface, it is known as **lava**. When lava cools, it forms solid rock.

As with earthquakes, there is a pattern to where volcanoes occur on Earth. Most are found at convergent or divergent plate boundaries, but they can also occur at seemingly random places far from plate boundaries.

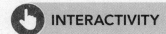
INTERACTIVITY

Explore how an erupting volcano might change Earth's surface.

Volcanism

Figure 1 The activity of volcanoes is called volcanism. Eruptions that release lava and other matter from Earth's interior can pose hazards to organisms, including humans. The natural system of volcanism also provides benefits for ecosystems.

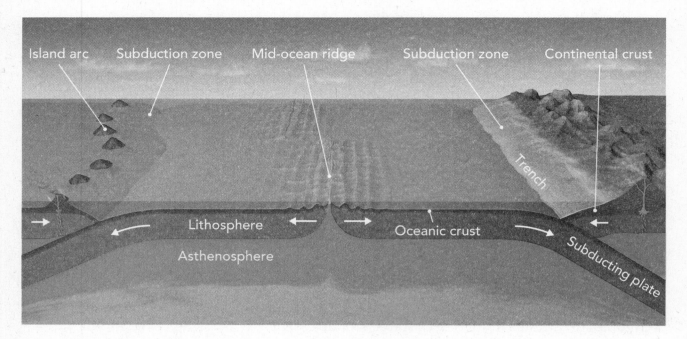

Island arc   Subduction zone   Mid-ocean ridge   Subduction zone   Continental crust

Trench

Lithosphere

Asthenosphere

Oceanic crust

Subducting plate

Divergent and Convergent Boundaries

Figure 2 Volcanic activity at plate boundaries can produce volcanoes on continents and volcanic island arcs.

SEP Construct Explanations Describe what is happening on the left side of the diagram, where ash is rising in the air over an active volcano.

....
....
....
....
....
....
....

HANDS-ON LAB

Investigate Explore moving volcanoes.

Volcanoes and Plate Boundaries

At convergent boundaries, the subduction of an oceanic plate under a continental plate can produce volcanoes along the edge of the continent. Subduction of an oceanic plate under an adjacent oceanic plate can result in a volcanic island arc. At divergent boundaries, molten magma comes through the crust as lava, which quickly hardens into rock, but if the volume of magma is especially large, then a volcanic cone may form. **Figure 2** summarizes these processes.

At Divergent Boundaries
Volcanoes form at divergent boundaries when plates move apart and rock rises to fill the vacant space. Most volcanoes at divergent boundaries occur in the ocean at mid-ocean ridges, so they are never seen. Only in places such as Iceland can you see ocean-ridge volcanoes. Less common are volcanoes, like Mt. Kilimanjaro, that occur at continental divergent boundaries such as the East African Rift.

At Convergent Boundaries
When a plate dives into the mantle in the process of subduction, trapped water leaves the sinking plate and mixes with the material of the overlying mantle, causing it to melt. The buoyant magma starts to rise toward the surface. If the magma reaches the surface before cooling, a volcano forms. If the overlying plate is part of the ocean floor, the resulting volcano begins to form on the seafloor as a seamount. If it grows large enough to break the ocean surface, it becomes a volcanic island. A chain of islands may form when volcanism occurs at multiple spots along the edge of an oceanic plate. This is called a volcanic island arc.

Hot Spot Volcanism

In addition to divergent and convergent plate boundaries, there is a third source of volcanoes: hot spots. A **hot spot** is an area where lava frequently erupts at the surface, independent of plate boundary processes. Most hot spots sit atop mantle plumes of hot rock. Hot spot plumes are fixed within the deep mantle. As a plate moves over the plume, a chain of volcanoes is created because older volcanoes keep being carried away from the hot spot. The many islands and seamounts of Hawaii have formed from the westward motion of the Pacific Plate, as is illustrated in **Figure 3**. Another hot spot is found at Yellowstone National Park in Wyoming. The "supervolcano" beneath the park may erupt again someday. During past giant eruptions of Yellowstone, the last one being 640,000 years ago, most of North America was covered with volcanic ash.

VIDEO

Learn more about volcanology.

CHECK POINT **Determine Conclusions** The Aleutian Islands of Alaska form a chain near a plate boundary. What type of boundary is it?

Model It!

Hot Spot Modeling

Figure 3 The Hawaiian Islands have formed from the movement of the Pacific Plate over a hot spot plume.

Integrate with Visuals

✏ Using the diagram as inspiration, design a functioning physical model of how a hot spot makes volcanoes on the ocean crust of a moving plate. Sketch or describe your model in the space here, including details on how it would work. Explain what became clear from working on the model that was not clear from your reading.

Composite Volcano

Figure 4 A composite volcano has alternating layers of hardened lava and ash.

SEP Develop Models ✏️
Complete the diagram by reading the description of the volcano's parts and writing in the missing labels.

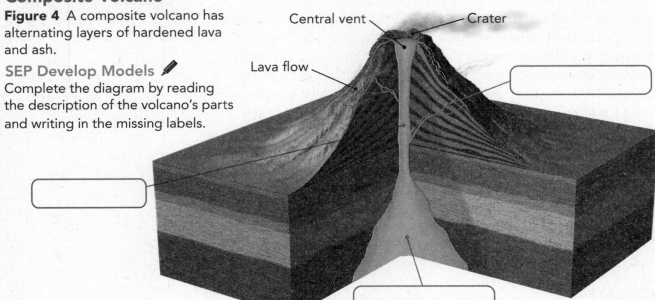

Central vent   Crater

Lava flow

Volcano Landforms

Literacy Connection

Integrate with Visuals
Use the diagram of the volcano to help you understand the text on this page.

Academic Vocabulary

Composite refers to something made of a mixture of different parts or elements. Many manufactured objects are made of composites—blends of different raw materials. How does this help you to understand what a composite volcano is?

....

....

....

....

Magma usually forms in the layer of hot rock in the upper mantle. Because magma is less dense than the rock around it, it moves upward to the surface. Once the magma exits a volcano and is exposed to air or water, it is called lava.

Volcano Parts Inside a volcano (**Figure 4**) is a system of passageways through which magma travels. Below the volcano is a magma chamber, where magma collects before an eruption. The volcano and surrounding landscape may swell slightly as the magma chamber fills. Magma moves up from the chamber through a pipe, which leads to the central vent—an opening at the top, which may be in a bowl-shaped crater. Some volcanoes have side vents, too. When lava flows out from a vent, it begins to cool and harden as it is pulled by gravity down the slope of the volcano. If lava is thrown explosively into the air, it hardens and falls to Earth in different forms. Bombs are large chunks of hardened lava. Cinders are the size of pebbles. The finest particles are called ash. The type of lava-based material that emerges from a new volcano defines the type of volcano that is built.

Volcano Types The volcano in **Figure 4** is a **composite** volcano. Also called a stratovolcano, it is made of alternating layers of lava flows and ash falls. These tend to be cone-shaped and tall. Mount Fuji in Japan is an example of a composite volcano. Other types of volcanic formations are shown in **Figure 5**.

Volcanic Formations

Figure 5 Volcanic activity can result in different landforms.

1. **Compare and Contrast** How are shield volcanoes and lava plateaus similar? How are they different?

....

....

....

2. **SEP Develop Models** ✎ Review the three steps of caldera formation. Finish the sentence to describe the second phase of caldera formation.

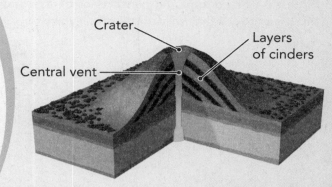

Cinder Cone Volcano If lava emerges from a new vent in Earth's crust as a mix of bombs, ash, and cinders, these materials build up into a cinder cone volcano. The loose, ashy material tends to erode quickly.

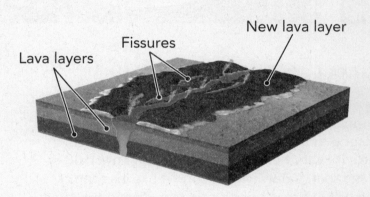

Lava Plateau Lava can flow out of several long cracks in Earth's crust and flood an area repeatedly over many years. Over time, these relatively flat layers of hardened lava build up into a lava plateau.

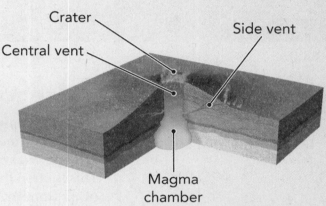

Shield Volcano Some volcanoes have slow, steady eruptions in which lava flows out and builds up over a broad area. Hot spot volcanoes tend to be shield volcanoes, and they can be massive.

Caldera A caldera forms when a volcano collapses on itself.

❶ Large eruptions empty the main vent and magma chamber of the volcano.

❷ Lacking support,

....

....

❸ A lake fills the caldera. Later eruptions form a small cone.

Lava from Quiet Eruptions

Figure 6 The content and consistency of lava determines the type of rock that will form as the lava cools.

INTERACTIVITY

Explore different volcanic landforms.

Academic Vocabulary

What does it mean if you have an active lifestyle?

....

....

....

Volcano Hazards

Volcanoes pose different hazards to humans and other organisms, mainly through eruptions. An **extinct**, or dead, volcano is a volcano that poses very little threat of eruption. This is often the case with hot-spot volcanoes that have drifted away from the hot spot. A **dormant** volcano is like a sleeping volcano—it poses little threat, but it could reawaken someday. **Active** volcanoes are the more immediate threat. Volcanologists classify eruptions as quiet or explosive. Whether an eruption is quiet or explosive depends in part on the magma's silica content and whether the magma is thin and runny or thick and sticky. Temperature helps determine how runny magma is.

Quiet Eruptions If the magma in a volcano's magma chamber is hot or low in silica, it will erupt quietly. The lava will be thin and runny, and trapped gases will bubble out gently. The consistency of the lava that emerges during a quiet eruption will affect how it looks and feels when it cools, as shown in **Figure 6**. Lava that is cooler and thicker, and moves slower forms rock with a rough surface consisting of jagged lava chunks. Fast-moving, hot lava that is thin and runny, forms rock that looks like a solid mass of ropelike coils.

The Hawaiian Islands continue to be produced mostly by quiet eruptions. Quiet eruptions are not necessarily safe. For example, the Hawaii Volcanoes National Park's visitors center was threatened in 1989 by a lava flow from Mount Kilauea.

Explosive Eruptions

Magma that has a large amount of silica will erupt more than magma containing little or no silica. High-silica magma is thick and sticky, causing it to build up in a pipe until pressure is so great that it bursts out over the surface. Trapped gases explode out instead of bubbling out gently. An explosion with that much force can hurl lava, ash, cinders, and bombs high into the atmosphere.

Krakatau, a volcano in a large volcanic arc in Indonesia, erupted in 1883. The eruption, depicted in **Figure 7**, was so violent that much of the the visible part of the island collapsed into the sea, producing a tsunami that killed 36,000 people. Gas and debris billowed more than 25 kilometers into the sky, and the sound from the explosion was heard 4,500 kilometers away. So much ash and sulfur dioxide was emitted into the atmosphere by the eruption that global temperatures were cooler for the following five years.

Krakatau Explodes

Figure 7 The eruption of Krakatau was a major disaster in Indonesia, but it affected the entire world as ash and sulfur dioxide entered the atmosphere.

Math Toolbox

Magma Composition

Magma is classified according to the amount of silica it contains. The less silica the magma contains, the more easily it flows. More silica makes magma stickier and thicker. Trapped gases can't emerge easily, so eruptions are explosive.

1. **Analyze Proportional Relationships** How do the two magma types compare in terms of silica content?

   ....

   ....

2. **SEP Construct Explanations** Which of the magma types would erupt more explosively? How would knowing the type of magma a volcano produces help nearby communities prepare for eruptions?

   ....

   ....

   ....

   ....

Types of Magma

Low-Silica

Silica 50% | Other oxides 47.5%

All other solids 2.5%

High-Silica

Silica 70% | Other oxides 27.5%

All other solids 2.5%

Measuring Gas Concentration

Figure 8 This device, called a spectrometer, can measure concentrations of volcanic gases by measuring how light passes through them. A high concentration of sulfur dioxide may mean an eruption is likely to occur.

INTERACTIVITY

Analyze how volcanic activity can change Earth's surface.

Predicting Volcano Hazards

Volcanologists use different tools to monitor volcanoes and predict eruptions. The gas emissions from volcanoes can be monitored to check for increases in sulfur dioxide, which may indicate that an eruption is coming **(Figure 8)**. Seismographs can detect rumblings deep inside a volcano that precede an eruption.

Volcanologists can also use devices to measure whether a volcano is swelling as its magma chamber fills up. These devices, called tiltmeters, are like carpenters' levels that detect very slight changes in the tilt of a volcano's slopes. If the tilt increases, it means the volcano is swelling and is likely to erupt. Telecommunications technology can transmit the data from these devices to scientists, who can then interpret the data and look for patterns associated with eruptions and notify the public if an eruption is predicted.

In areas with known volcanic hazards, engineering solutions, such as placing artificial barriers to divert lava and mudflows, may be utilized to help reduce the effects of an eruption. Public utilities, such as electricity, are also impacted during eruptions. To reduce the effects and maintain power to local communities, some utility companies are investigating ways to redesign their wooden utility poles to protect them from the extreme heat.

☑ **CHECK POINT** **Cite Textual Evidence** If sulfur dioxide concentrations emitted from a volcano increase from less than one part per million (ppm) to 4 ppm, is the volcano more or less likely to erupt soon?

....

....

Question It !

Building on a Volcano

In some parts of the world, building on a volcano is a necessity because most of the land is volcanic. Suppose you had to build a home on a volcanic island. **SEP Ask Questions** What questions would you want to answer before choosing a specific site for construction?

....

....

....

....

....

....

MS-ESS2-2, MS-ESS3-2

1. **Identify Phenomena** Runny lava oozes from the vent of a broad, gently-sloping shield volcano. What type of eruption is this?

....

2. **SEP Construct Explanations** Why do volcanoes form at divergent and convergent boundaries?

....

....

....

....

....

....

3. **CCC Patterns** The Hawaiian Islands formed as the Pacific Plate moved west-northwest over a hot spot. In which part of the islands would you expect to find the most active volcanoes? Dormant and extinct volcanoes? Explain.

....

....

....

....

....

....

....

4. **SEP Interpret Data** You are sailing in the South Pacific Ocean, far from any plate boundary. Looming on the horizon is a dark, broad, rounded island with sparse vegetation. A few thin flows of orange lava drip into the sea. Some smoky vapor unfurls from the center of the island. What kind of volcano is this? Explain.

....

....

....

....

....

5. **CCC Structure and Function** How are volcanic island arcs formed?

....

....

....

....

....

....

....

....

....

Quest CHECK-IN

In this lesson, you learned about the connection between plate tectonics and volcanoes.

SEP Analyze Data Why is it important to understand the type of volcano Mount Rainier is and the patterns of activity at the nearest plate boundary?

....

....

....

HANDS-ON LAB

Signs of Eruption?

Go online to download the lab and identify signs of a volcanic eruption.

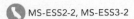

MS-ESS2-2, MS-ESS3-2

Evidence-Based Assessment

In 2011, a magnitude 9.0 earthquake occurred in the ocean floor off the east coast of Japan. Tsunameter buoys and tide gauges recorded tsunami waves as they crossed the Pacific Ocean. Scientists used the data to predict how large the waves would be and when they would arrive at different locations. The map shown represents the tsunami forecast model for the event, which was used by coastal communities around the Pacific to prepare for local impacts of the tsunami.

Analyze the map of the 2011 tsunami wave forecast. Keep in mind the following information:

- The triangles symbolize specific tsunameter buoys, which measure wave height, or amplitude.

- The numbered contour lines represent how many hours after the earthquake the tsunami waves were forecast to reach those areas of the ocean.

- Major plate boundaries are indicated on the map.

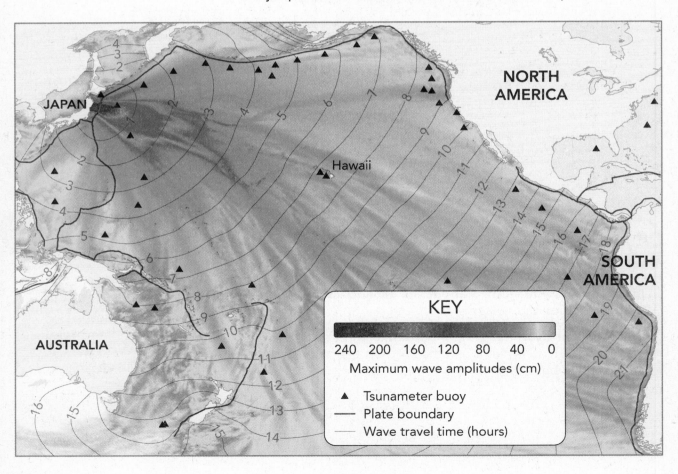

1. **SEP Analyze Data** According to the data, where was tsunami wave height expected to be greatest?

   A. Australia   **B.** Japan

   C. North America   **D.** South America

2. **SEP Interpret Data** What can you observe about the impact of the earthquake on Australia? Select all that apply.

   ☐ The tsunami waves reached Australia about 9 hours after the earthquake.

   ☐ Maximum wave amplitude was between 80 cm and 120 cm.

   ☐ Tsunami waves reached Australia and Hawaii at the same time.

   ☐ Australia was not impacted by the earthquake in Japan.

   ☐ Tsunami waves hit Australia about 10 hours before they hit South America.

3. **Model Phenomena** When was the tsunami expected to reach northern California, and what was the expected wave height?

   ....

   ....

   ....

   ....

4. **CCC Cause and Effect** Arrange the following events in order from 1 to 5 to describe how the motion of tectonic plates can result in a tsunami, with 1 being the first event and 5 being the last.

Events	Order
A tsunami is formed and can impact surrounding areas.	
Tectonic plates move toward each other for long periods of time.	
Energy lifts a large volume of water.	
Two plates at a fault slip and release the energy, causing an earthquake.	
Stress builds up at a fault under the water.	

5. **SEP Construct Explanations** In terms of their usefulness to society in protecting human lives, why are so many tsunameters placed along coastlines of the Pacific Ocean? Provide two explanations for this use of new technology.

....

....

....

....

....

....

....

....

....

....

Quest FINDINGS

Complete the Quest!

Present information on Mount Rainier's history and current geological research, along with your evidence-based argument about whether it is safe to hike and camp there.

Reason Quantitatively What data will help you to predict whether Mount Rainier could erupt while you are on a two-week camping trip nearby? Explain.

....

....

....

👆 **INTERACTIVITY**

Reflect on Mount Rainier's Safety

Modeling Sea-Floor Spreading

How can you prevent a major oil spill by **designing** and building a model that **demonstrates** sea-floor spreading?

Background

Phenomenon Imagine you are a marine geologist reviewing a plan to construct an undersea oil pipeline. You notice that part of the pipeline will cross a mid-ocean ridge. In this investigation, you will design and build a model that demonstrates sea-floor spreading to show why this plan is not a good idea.

Materials

(per group)
- scissors
- transparent tape
- colored pencil or marker
- metric ruler
- 2 sheets of unlined letter-sized paper
- manila folder

Safety

Be sure to follow all safety guidelines provided by your teacher. The Safety Appendix of your textbook provides more details about the safety icons.

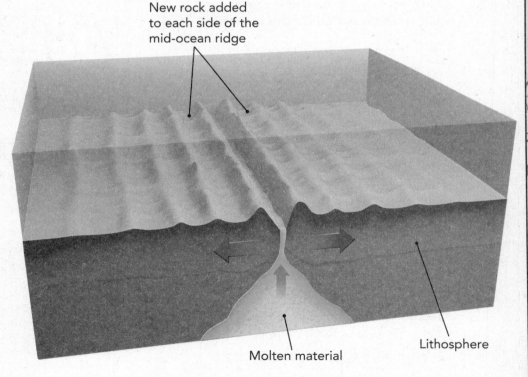

New rock added to each side of the mid-ocean ridge

Molten material

Lithosphere

Design Your Model and Investigation

Discuss with your group why building a pipeline that spans a mid-ocean ridge is a bad idea. Over time, what will happen to the pipeline?

With your group, take a look at the materials. How can you use the materials to construct a model that demonstrates why the pipeline plan is a problem?

HANDS-ON LAB

и**Demonstrate** Go online for a downloadable worksheet of this lab.

Consider the following questions:

- How can you use the manila folder to represent the mantle?

- How can you use the two pieces of plain letter-sized paper to create matching strips of striped sea floor?

- How can you represent the mid-ocean ridge and the subduction zones on either side of the ridge?

Use the space provided to sketch your group's model and write notes for guiding its construction. Have your teacher approve your group's plan, and then construct and demonstrate the model.

Sketch of Model

Design Notes

_____
_____
_____
_____
_____
_____
_____
_____
_____
_____
_____
_____
_____
_____

Analyze and Interpret Data

1. **SEP Develop Models** Why is it important that your model have identical patterns of stripes on both sides of the center slit?

....

....

....

....

2. **SEP Construct Explanations** Use evidence from your model to support the claim that sea-floor spreading builds two different tectonic plates.

....

....

....

....

3. **SEP Refine Your Solution** Look at the models created by other groups. How are the other solutions different? How might you revise your group's model to better demonstrate sea-floor spreading? Think of how your own and other class models improved your understanding of sea-floor spreading after you completed reading the lessons.

....

....

....

....

4. **SEP Use Models** How could your group revise the model to reinforce the idea that the amount of crust that forms at the mid-ocean ridge is equal to the amount of crust recycled back into the mantle at subduction zones?

....

....

....

5. **CCC Stability and Change** How does your model support the claim that building an oil pipeline across a divergent boundary would be a bad idea? What effects might there be on marine ecosystems?

....

....

....

Distribution of Natural Resources

Investigative Phenomenon
How can you explain the uneven distributions of Earth's natural resources?

MS-ESS3-1 Construct a scientific explanation based on evidence for how the uneven distributions of Earth's mineral, energy, and groundwater resources are the result of past and current geoscience processes.

EP&Clc Students should be developing an understanding that the quality, quantity, and reliability of the goods and ecosystem services provided by natural systems are directly affected by the health of those systems.

HOW did this gold
get in this rock?

Connect Observe coal to draw
conclusions about its formation.

What questions do you have about the phenomenon?

....
....
....
....
....
....
....
....
....
....

Nonrenewable Energy Resources

MS-ESS3-1 Construct a scientific explanation based on evidence for how the uneven distributions of Earth's mineral, energy, and groundwater resources are the result of past and current geoscience processes. (Also **EP&CIc**)

Connect It!

✎ **Identify and label some the materials that are being used in this construction project.**

Classify Pick one of the materials you identified in the photo and explain whether you think the resource is limited or unlimited.

....

....

Natural Resources

We all rely on natural resources to live and work (**Figure 1**). A **natural resource** is anything occuring naturally in the environment that humans use. We need air to breathe, water to drink, soil in which to grow plants to eat, sunlight to make those plants grow, and other natural resources. Some of these resources are essentially unlimited and renewable regardless of what we do. For example, sunlight and wind are available daily at most places on Earth. Other renewable resources can be reused or replenished, but it may require some care or planning. For example, wood from trees is a renewable resource as long as some trees are spared to reproduce and make the next generation of trees.

Other resources are **nonrenewable resources,** which cannot be replaced. This may be because there is a finite amount of the resource on Earth and we don't have a way to make more of it. The element silver, for example, cannot be made from other substances. The amount of silver on Earth is set. Other resources are considered nonrenewable because it takes very long periods of time for them to form.

✓ CHECK POINT **Cite Evidence** Why is wood considered to be a renewable resource?

....

....

....

HANDS-ON LAB

Classify resources that you use in a typical day.

📖 **Reflect** In your science notebook, describe how a natural resource could shift from being renewable to nonrenewable.

Resource Use
Figure 1 This construction project in Los Angeles, California, relies on a number of natural resources.

Lignite

Bituminous Coal

Anthracite

Types of Coal

Figure 2 Brittle, lustrous anthracite has more energy than crumbly, dull lignite.

Determine Differences Why might one type of coal contain more energy than another type of coal?

....

....

....

....

Fossil Fuels

The sources of energy commonly called fossil fuels include coal, petroleum, and natural gas. **Fossil fuels** are the energy-rich substances made from the preserved remains of organisms. The chemical energy in fossil fuels can be converted to other forms by burning them.

The energy stored in these compounds originally arrived on Earth as sunlight. Photosynthetic organisms such as algae, moss, grasses, and trees converted sunlight into carbon-based compounds. When animals ate the plants, they absorbed some of those compounds. Under certain conditions involving high temperatures and pressures, the remains of these organisms were transformed into new materials, including solid coal, liquid petroleum, and methane gas.

Coal Coal is formed from the remains of plants that died long ago in and around swampy areas. There are different grades, or types, of coal (**Figure 2**). Each grade forms under different conditions, as shown in **Figure 3**. In addition to being a source of energy, coal is used in a wide array of applications. Coal is used in water and air purification systems, as well as medical equipment such as kidney dialysis devices. Coal is used to make steel from iron ore.

Burning coal in coal-fired power plants accounts for about 30 percent of the electricity produced in the United States. Coal has long been used as a fuel because it has twice as much energy per unit of mass as wood. So, when coal can be mined at a large scale, it can be an efficient source of energy.

Unfortunately, burning coal produces pollutants and causes millions of deaths each year from health problems. Coal mining also requires large mines to be dug into the ground, or the removal of mountaintops or other surface layers to access coal beds. Removing coal causes great damage to the surrounding environment, threatening other types of natural resources and the ecosystem services they provide.

☑ CHECK POINT **Determine Central Ideas** What is the original source of the energy contained in coal? Explain.

....

....

....

Coal Formation and Distribution

Figure 3 Coal only forms under the right conditions. The map shows major deposits of coal around the world.

1. **SEP Use Models** ✏ Circle the three continents that have the most coal resources.

2. **SEP Construct Explanations** Why is coal not evenly distributed around the world?

....

....

....

....

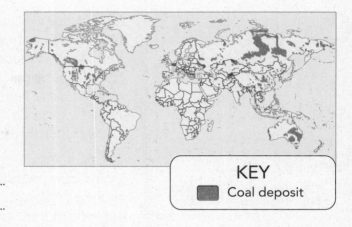

KEY
⬛ Coal deposit

Swamp Environment

PEAT
(Partially altered plant material; very smoky when burned, low energy)

Burial

LIGNITE
(Soft, brown coal; moderate energy)

Compaction

Greater burial

BITUMINOUS COAL
(Soft, black coal; major coal used in power generation and industry; high energy)

Compaction

Metamorphism

ANTHRACITE
(Hard, black coal; used in industry; highest energy)

Stress

65

INTERACTIVITY

Explore the distribution of different fossil fuels.

VIDEO

Learn more about how fossil fuels form underground.

Oil What we commonly refer to as oil is scientifically known as **petroleum**, from the Latin terms *petra* (rock) and *oleum* (oil). Petroleum is made of the remains of small animals, algae, and other organisms that lived in marine environments hundreds of millions of years ago. Oil deposits form when these remains become trapped underground and are subject to high pressure and temperature.

Because it is a liquid and can be processed into different fuels, petroleum is especially useful for powering engines in automobiles, ships, trains, and airplanes. Petroleum also has many important industrial uses, such as making plastics, lubricants, and fertilizers. Petroleum is also the basis for synthetic fibers, such as rayon, carbon fiber, and nylon. Many cosmetic and pharmaceutical products, such as petroleum jelly and tar shampoos that treat dandruff, contain forms of petroleum.

As with coal, burning oil and natural gas emits carbon dioxide. Oil can also be spilled, which can be disastrous for wildlife and water quality (**Figure 4**). Natural gas leaks contribute to global warming, and can result in explosions if the concentration of gas is high and a spark ignites it.

Oil Impacts

Figure 4 Oil is often drilled from the ocean floor and transported by ship. Major oil spills can harm or kill wildlife, as well as damage habitats and water quality.

1. **SEP Interpret Data** What are the two major causes of accidental oil spills?

2. **SEP Use Mathematics** About how much more oil was spilled as a result of the Deepwater Horizon explosion than the *Valdez* running aground?

Location and Date	Amount Spilled (gallons)	Cause
Santa Barbara, California, 1969	4 million	Blown-out offshore oil drilling platform
Trinidad and Tobago, 1979	90 million	Collision of two oil tanker ships
Gulf of Mexico, 1979	140 million	Blown-out *Ixtoc 1* oil well on ocean floor, fire, collapse of drilling platform
Persian Gulf, 1983	80 million	Collision of ship with oil-drilling platform during Iraq-Iran war
Prince William Sound, Alaska, 1989	11 million	*Exxon Valdez* oil tanker ship runs aground, puncturing hull
Gulf of Mexico, 2010	181 million	Blown-out Deepwater Horizon oil well, explosion of platform

Petroleum Formation and Distribution

Figure 5 Petroleum has been drilled for all over the world. Wells or rigs are constructed to tap "fields" of oil hundreds or thousands of meters below Earth's surface, both on land and water.

SEP Engage in Argument ✏ A large sea once existed in the United States. Shade the area of the country where you think the sea likely existed. Then explain your choice.

....

....

....

KEY
☐ Onshore basins
☐ Offshore basins

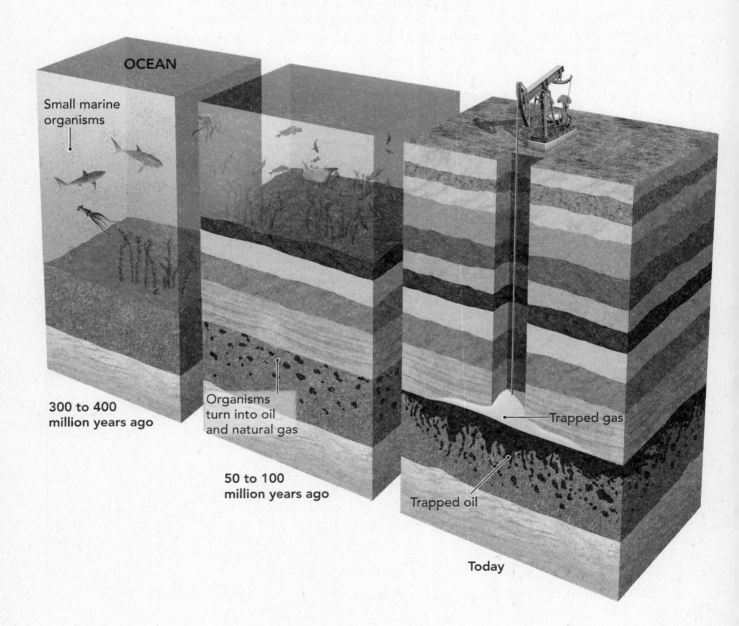

OCEAN

Small marine organisms

300 to 400 million years ago

Organisms turn into oil and natural gas

50 to 100 million years ago

Trapped gas

Trapped oil

Today

Fracking

Figure 6 Groundwater samples taken from sites where fracking has occurred have tested positive for methane and other hydrocarbons.

Natural Gas Formed from the same processes that produce oil and found in the same locations, natural gas is trapped in pockets within layers of rock deep below Earth's surface. A drill can tap the trapped gas, and then pipelines carry the gas for processing and transport. Burning petroleum and coal releases more carbon dioxide than burning natural gas. This is one reason many countries have encouraged more use of natural gas and are surveying underground basins of gas for further exploitation. On the other hand, the gas itself is a powerful greenhouse gas that contributes to global warming. This means any leaks of natural gas from wells, pipelines, and other structures pose a significant pollution problem.

To meet the demand for natural gas, a process called *fracking* has become popular. Fracking, which works for both oil and gas, is short for hydraulic fracturing. This involves using pressured fluids to break layers of shale rock and force out the trapped natural gas, which can then be collected and transported. There are concerns that the fracking fluids are contaminating vital stores of groundwater that humans rely on (**Figure 6**) and natural systems whose health is important to human activities.

☑ CHECK POINT **Cite Textual Evidence** Natural gas burns cleaner than coal, yet it is considered a pollutant. Why?

....

....

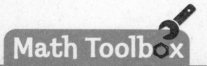

Math Toolbox

Natural Gas Consumption in the U.S.

In recent years, consumption patterns of natural gas have changed.

1. **SEP Use Mathematics** What was the percent increase in gas usage from 1980 to 2015? Show your work.

....

....

2. **Analyze Relationships** What trend is shown in the data?

....

....

3. **CCC Cause and Effect** What factors contributed to the trend shown in the data?

....

....

U.S. Annual Natural Gas Consumption	
Year	Volume (Million Cubic Meters)
1980	562,862
1985	489,342
1990	542,935
1995	628,829
2000	660,720
2005	623,379
2010	682,062
2015	773,228

Source: U.S. Energy Information Administration

Nuclear Energy

Nuclear power is another nonrenewable energy resource used to generate much of the world's electricity. Nuclear energy provides 20 percent of the electricity in the United States. Inside a nuclear power plant, controlled nuclear fission reactions occur. **Nuclear fission** is the splitting of an atom's nucleus into two nuclei. Fission releases a great deal of energy. This energy is used to heat water, turning it into steam. The steam is then used to turn the blades of a turbine to produce electricity.

Uranium is the fuel used for nuclear fission inside nuclear reactors. It is a heavy metal that occurs in most rocks and is usually extracted through mining. The uranium found on Earth was part of the original cloud of dust and gas from which our solar system formed. Uranium is found throughout Earth's crust. But large ores of the material are formed from geological processes that only occur in certain locations on Earth (**Figure 7**).

Literacy Connection

Cite Textual Evidence As you read, underline text that supports the idea that uranium is a limited resource with finite amounts on Earth.

Source: World Nuclear Association

Distribution of Uranium

Figure 7 According to the World Nuclear Association, almost 70 percent of accessible uranium is found in only 5 countries.

1. **SEP Use Models** ✏ Circle the two countries with the greatest percentage of uranium resources.

2. **CCC Patterns** What patterns do you observe in the distribution of uranium?

....

....

....

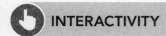

INTERACTIVITY

Learn more about the progression of living matter to petroleum.

Using Energy Resources

Fossil fuels are among the most important nonrenewable resources for humans. As the human population has grown, these resources have become less abundant. Geologists estimate that we have already used about half the petroleum that fossilization, pressure, heat, and time have produced over hundreds of millions of years—and all in just a few centuries.

Pollution Humans are burning fossil fuels at a faster rate than the resulting carbon emissions can be absorbed by natural processes, such as photosynthesis. This is why the concentration of carbon dioxide in the atmosphere is now 45 percent higher than it was just over 200 years ago. Scientists have concluded that this is fueling global warming and climate change.

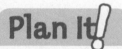

Household Energy Use

SEP Plan an Investigation Use the space to describe how you could determine how much fossil fuel is used in your home and then make recommendations about how to reduce your usage.

....
....
....
....
....
....
....
....
....
....
....
....
....
....
....
....

World Politics The uneven distribution of fossil fuel resources has led to political problems, including war. In 1990, Iraq invaded neighboring Kuwait in part because of disagreements over how oil fields at a shared border should be used. When the United States and other nations came to Kuwait's defense and drove out the Iraqi forces, oil fields and wells were set on fire. This resulted in hundreds of millions of gallons of oil being burned or spilled, and untreated emissions billowing into the atmosphere (**Figure 8**).

☑ CHECK POINT **Determine Conclusions** How have human activities affected the distribution of fossil fuels on Earth?

....

....

....

....

....

Gulf War Oil Fires
Figure 8 The oil fields that were set on fire during the first Gulf War in 1991 caused significant damage to the land and living things.

☑LESSON 1 Check

MS-ESS3-1, EP&Clc

1. Identify Which fossil fuel is produced from the remains of peat?

....

2. CCC Cause and Effect A friend argues that the location of a petroleum deposit is a sign that marine organisms once lived there. Is your friend correct? Explain.

....
....
....
....
....
....
....
....
....

3. Apply Scientific Reasoning How does the abundance of a resource, and whether it is renewable or nonrenewable, affect how much it is used?

....
....
....
....
....
....
....
....
....
....
....
....

4. SEP Engage in Argument What advantage does coal have over wood as an energy source? What is the major disadvantage of using coal for energy?

....
....
....
....
....
....
....
....
....
....

5. SEP Construct Explanations Why are oil, coal, and natural gas not found evenly distributed on Earth?

....
....
....
....
....
....
....
....
....
....
....
....
....

Micro-Hydro
POWER

▶ VIDEO

Examine how hydroelectric power plants and wind farms generate clean energy.

How can people without access to electricity use moving water to generate power? You engineer it!

The Challenge: To generate power from moving water.

Earth's water system is an excellent source of power. Centuries ago, people realized that moving water, properly channeled, can turn wheels that make machinery move. More recently, engineers designed large-scale dams to harness the energy of moving water. Water power's great advantage is that the water is always moving, so electricity can be generated 24 hours a day.

Now engineers have developed hydropower on a small scale, known as micro-hydro power. If there is a small river or stream running through your property, then you need only a few basic things: a turbine, pipes to channel the water to the turbine, and a generator that will transform the energy into electricity.

Harness it!

Channel it!

Wire it!

Spin it!

In this micro-hydro system, water from the river is channeled to the generator, which transforms the energy of the moving water into electrical energy.

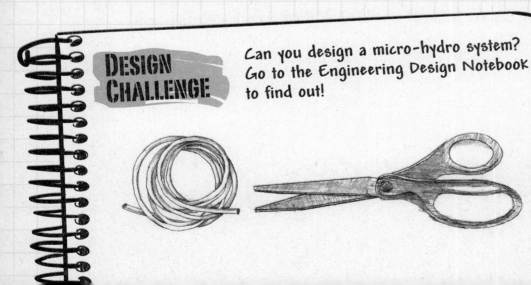

DESIGN CHALLENGE

Can you design a micro-hydro system? Go to the Engineering Design Notebook to find out!

uInvestigate Explore the geological processes that form minerals.

MS-ESS3-1 Construct a scientific explanation based on evidence for how the uneven distributions of Earth's mineral, energy, and groundwater resources are the result of past and current geoscience processes. (Also **EP&CIc**)

Connect It !

✏ **Circle some of the objects in the photo that you think contain minerals.**

SEP Construct Explanations How do you think these minerals formed?

....

....

....

Minerals and Ores

You may think that minerals are only found in rocks. It's true that rocks are made from minerals, but if you look around, you will probably see many other things that are made from minerals. Metals are made from one or more minerals. The graphite in a pencil is a type of mineral. Computers, smartphones, and other electronic devices are made with metals and other minerals, too. Even you contain minerals, such as the calcium-bearing minerals that make up your bones and teeth.

But what is a mineral? A mineral is a solid substance that is non-living and made from a particular combination of elements. There are over 5,000 named minerals on Earth. Gold, quartz, and talc are just a few examples. When a mixture of a mineral and the surrounding rock is large enough and valuable enough for it to be extracted from the ground, it is known as **ore**. People remove ore from the ground and refine it, a process that separates the minerals from the rock. They can then use or sell the minerals to make money.

HANDS-ON LAB

Investigate Explore the geological processes that form minerals.

Reflect Throughout the day, list some of the things you see and use that are made from minerals. Then, at the end of the day, write a paragraph explaining why minerals are important and describing some of their most important uses.

Stalactite Formation
Figure 1 These stalactites in Carlsbad Caverns National Park in New Mexico formed as minerals deposited by a dripping mineral-rich solution built up over long periods of time.

How Minerals Form

Minerals form in different ways. They can form from organic materials, from mineral-rich solutions, and from cooling magma and lava.

Organic Material Corals like the ones in **Figure 2** create a hard outer skeleton that provides the coral with shape and protection. This skeleton is made from thin layers of calcium carbonate (also called the mineral calcite), a chemical compound similar to the shells of other sea animals. Once the coral is dead, the calcium carbonate skeleton is left behind. It may get buried and broken down into smaller fragments.

Minerals from Living Things

Figure 2 These corals produce a hard outer skeleton made from the mineral calcite. The skeleton will be around for a long time after the coral dies.

Apply Concepts Why wouldn't other body parts of living things, such as skin, become minerals after an organism's death?

....

....

Solutions When water contains dissolved substances it is called a solution. In some cases, the substances in these solutions will **crystallize** to form a new mineral. This can happen within bodies of water and underground. One way this happens on Earth's surface involves the process of evaporation. When the water evaporates, the elements and compounds that are left behind crystallize into new minerals such as salts. This is how the mineral formations in **Figure 3** formed.

Another way that minerals form from solutions is through a process in which a warm solution flows through a crack in existing rock. Elements and compounds leave the solution as it cools and crystallize as minerals in the crack. These form veins of ores that are different from the surrounding rock.

Magma and Lava The molten and semi-molten rock mixture found beneath Earth's surface is known as magma. In its molten, or melted state, magma is very hot. But when it cools, it hardens into solid rock. This rock is made from crystallized minerals. It may form beneath Earth's surface or above Earth's surface when magma (which is known as lava when it breaks the surface) erupts from the ground and then cools and hardens as is shown in **Figure 4.**

The types of minerals that form from magma and lava vary based on the materials and gases in the magma, as well as the rate at which it cools.

✓ CHECK POINT **Analyze Text Structure** Examine the way the text on these two pages has been organized. Describe how the author has organized the text so that it supports the reader's comprehension.

....

....

....

....

....

....

Minerals from Solutions
Figure 3 These mineral deposits in Mammoth Hot Springs in Yellowstone National Park formed from a solution.

SEP Analyze Data ✏ Draw an X on the solution the minerals formed from. Circle some of the mineral deposits.

Minerals from Magma
Figure 4 As this lava cools, it will harden and crystallize into minerals.

CCC Cause and Effect Where would you expect to find minerals that have formed in this way?

....

....

....

Gold Rush

Figure 5 California's geological history produced mineral-rich rock and soil. The discovery of gold in the state resulted in the Gold Rush of 1849.

Academic Vocabulary

Explain what *distributed* means and give one or two examples of something that is distributed.

....

....

....

Distribution of Minerals The distribution of mineral resources on Earth depends on how and when the minerals form. Common minerals, such as the ones that make up most of the rocks in Earth's crust, are found roughly evenly distributed around the planet. Other minerals are rare because they only form as a result of tremendous heat and pressure near volcanic systems. Therefore, these minerals will only be found near subduction zones or other regions associated with volcanic activity. Other minerals may form from evaporation in the ocean or on land, such as in basins called playas. The map in **Figure 6** shows how some minerals are **distributed** around the world.

Gold, for example, is a heavy metal that formed, along with all other atoms other than hydrogen and helium, from stars that went supernova preceding the formation of our solar system. Gold is rare at the surface because most of it sank into the core when the early Earth was molten. Gold gets concentrated when hot fluids pass through the crust and pick up the gold, which doesn't fit well in the crystals of most rocks.

☑ CHECK POINT **Determine Meaning** Locate the term *concentrated* in the second paragraph. Using context clues, what do you think this word means? Explain your thinking.

....

....

....

Question It!

Minerals for Dinner?
Minerals are used in many ways in our everyday lives. We even need minerals in our diets to stay healthy. Humans need minerals that contain calcium, potassium, and magnesium to grow, fight illness, and carry out everyday functions.

Apply Scientific Reasoning Write two or three questions you would like to have answered about the importance of minerals in your diet.

....

....

....

....

....

....

....

....

....

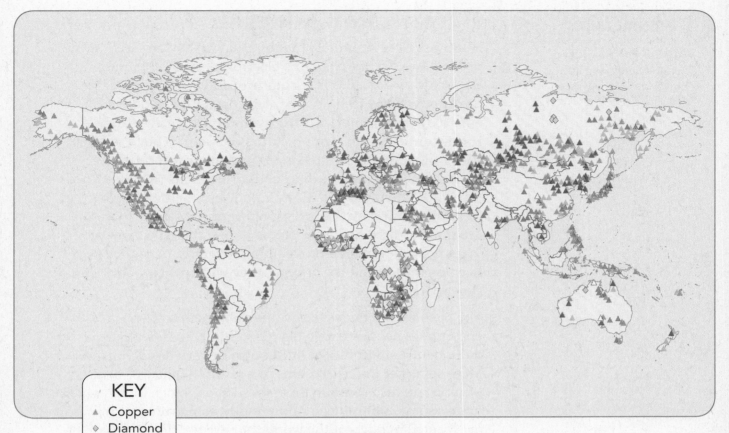

KEY

▲ Copper
◇ Diamond
▲ Gold
▲ Iron
▲ Lead-Zinc
▲ Silver
△ Uranium

Mineral Distribution

Figure 6 Minerals are distributed unevenly on Earth.

1. **Claim** Which part of the United States is the richest in gold and other mineral resources?

....

2. **Evidence** 🖊 Circle the area on the map that provides evidence to support your claim.

3. **Reasoning** Suppose you were to draw the boundaries of tectonic plates and locations of volcanic activity on the map. What patterns would you notice among plate boundaries, volcanic activity, and the distribution of different mineral resources? How do these patterns relate to California's mineral resources? Explain.

....
....
....
....
....
....
....
....
....

INTERACTIVITY

Find out more about mineral resources and their distributions.

VIDEO

Learn why some minerals are only found in certain places.

INTERACTIVITY

Explore the use of the mineral limestone as a building material.

Humans and Minerals

Humans rely on minerals in many ways. They are used in the production of buildings, cars, electronics, and other materials we use every day. Jewelry, sculpture, and other works of art are often made with minerals, such as marble, jade, and emerald. Some minerals are easy and inexpensive to get. For instance, bananas are high in potassium. They are also plentiful, affordable, and easy to find in any grocery store. Other minerals, such as diamonds or benitoite (**Figure 7**), are rare and difficult to get. Many valuable minerals are removed from the ground by the process of mining. As more minerals are mined, there are fewer places to find them because they are a nonrenewable resource. In other words, once they have been removed from the ground, they will not grow back any time soon.

The push to find deposits of valuable minerals often encourages people to take big risks. Mining can not only damage the environment, it can also be very dangerous work. Mine collapses and explosions can result in injury or death. Mining can also result in illnesses such as "black lung," which affects some coal miners. Additionally, some valuable minerals are located in parts of the world that are politically unstable. When companies attempt to mine for these minerals there, it can cause problems and danger for everyone involved.

☑ CHECK POINT **Summarize Text** How do humans rely on minerals?

....

....

....

Rare Mineral

Figure 7 Benitoite is a very rare blue mineral that forms as a result of hydrothermal processes in Earth's crust. It has been discovered in a few locations on Earth. But gemstone-quality benitoite can be found in only one place in California.

Connect to Society
Do you think a benitoite ring would be costly or inexpensive? Explain your reasoning.

....

....

....

....

....

....

☑ LESSON 2 Check

MS-ESS3-1, EP&Clc

1. Define What are minerals? List examples.

....
....
....
....
....
....
....
....

2. SEP Construct Explanations Explain the relationship between minerals and ores.

....
....
....
....
....
....
....
....
....
....

3. CCC Cause and Effect What causes minerals to be unevenly distributed on Earth?

....
....
....
....
....
....
....
....
....
....

4. CCC Patterns ✏ Use drawings to show one of the ways that minerals can form.

LESSON

(3) Water Resources

HANDS-ON LAB

иInvestigate Model how an artesian well accesses groundwater.

MS-ESS3-1 Construct a scientific explanation based on evidence for how the uneven distributions of Earth's mineral, energy, and groundwater resources are the result of past and current geoscience processes. (Also **EP&Cic**)

Connect It !

✎ **The drop of water on Earth represents all the water on the planet. Draw a circle inside the drop of water to represent the amount of fresh water you think exists on Earth.**

CCC Systems How does water's role in Earth systems make it an important natural resource?

....

....

....

Water on Earth

Although Earth is known as the water planet, the water that living things rely on represents only a fraction of the planet's total water supply **(Figure 1)**. Most water on Earth is salt water. Fresh water is only found on the surface of our planet as surface ice or water, or within Earth's crust as groundwater.

Water is a limited resource, which means there is a finite amount of it on Earth. In addition, it is not evenly distributed around the planet as a result of meteorological and geological forces. The water cycle circulates water through Earth's ocean and other bodies of water, on and below its surface, and in the atmosphere. A very small amount of the water on the surface of the planet is immediately available for human use in lakes and rivers, but most fresh water is locked up as ice at the poles and in glaciers.

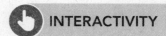

INTERACTIVITY

Predict how much water on Earth is drinkable.

Reflect How is water used in your local environment? In your science notebook, describe some ways your local environment would be affected if there were suddenly less water available.

A Drop to Drink
Figure 1 If all of the water on Earth were collected, it would form a sphere about 1,380 kilometers (860 miles) across.

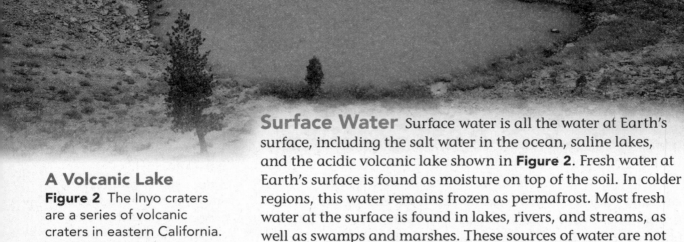

A Volcanic Lake

Figure 2 The Inyo craters are a series of volcanic craters in eastern California. Small lakes have formed in some of these craters.

SEP Construct Explanations How do you think the water ended up in the lake?

....

....

....

....

Surface Water Surface water is all the water at Earth's surface, including the salt water in the ocean, saline lakes, and the acidic volcanic lake shown in **Figure 2**. Fresh water at Earth's surface is found as moisture on top of the soil. In colder regions, this water remains frozen as permafrost. Most fresh water at the surface is found in lakes, rivers, and streams, as well as swamps and marshes. These sources of water are not evenly distributed across Earth. Precipitation, which depends on factors such as atmospheric patterns and temperature, determines where surface water forms.

Most of the fresh water at Earth's surface is found in lakes. Lakes form through various geological processes when water fills in depressions in Earth's surface. These can occur as a result of erosion, the movement of tectonic plates, and retreating glaciers. Some lakes form when a river's path erodes away an area or a dam blocks a river's flow. All rivers begin as a small flow of water caused by gravity. Runoff from rain or melting ice collects and flows downhill following the least resistant path. These small flows of water form streams, which combine and grow to form larger rivers and river systems.

Math Toolbox

Distribution of Water Resources

While most of the planet is covered in water, only a small amount of it is available to humans for cooking, drinking, and bathing.

1. **SEP Develop Models** Use the data in the graphs to complete the missing values.

2. **Draw Comparative Inferences** About how much more accessible surface fresh water is found in lakes than in the atmosphere as water vapor?

....

....

....

....

....

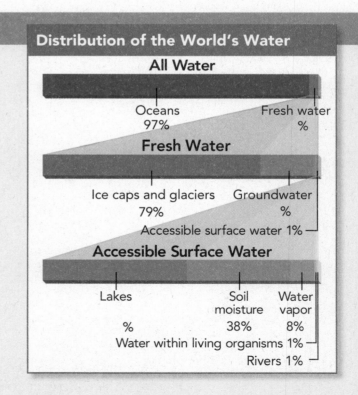

Distribution of the World's Water

All Water

Oceans 97%   Fresh water %

Fresh Water

Ice caps and glaciers 79%   Groundwater %

Accessible surface water 1% —

Accessible Surface Water

Lakes   Soil moisture   Water vapor

%   38%   8%

Water within living organisms 1% —

Rivers 1% —

Groundwater

Groundwater As with fresh water at the surface, groundwater is not evenly distributed across Earth **(Figure 3)**. The presence of groundwater depends on the type of rock layers in Earth's crust. Groundwater forms when gravity causes water from precipitation and runoff to seep into the ground and fill the empty spaces between these rocks. Some rocks are more porous, or have more empty spaces in which water can collect. The volume of porous rock that can contain groundwater is called an aquifer. Wells are drilled into aquifers to access the water.

Deep groundwater reservoirs can take hundreds or thousands of years to accumulate, especially in arid regions where there is little rainfall or surface water to supply the aquifer. New studies of Earth's mantle reveal there may be many oceans' worth of water locked hundreds of kilometers below the surface in mineral formations. This groundwater may take millions of years to exchange with surface water through the movement of tectonic plates and mantle convection.

✓ **CHECK POINT** **Summarize** How does the type of rock in Earth's crust affect the distribution of groundwater?

....

....

....

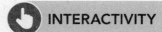

INTERACTIVITY

Explore how groundwater is distributed around Earth.

HANDS-ON LAB

и**Investigate** Model how an artesian well accesses groundwater.

Distribution of Groundwater

Figure 3 Groundwater is especially important in areas that do not have immediate access to rivers or lakes for sources of fresh water.

SEP Use Models ✏
Indicate the areas on the map with the greatest groundwater resources with a circle. Indicate the areas with the least groundwater resources with an X.

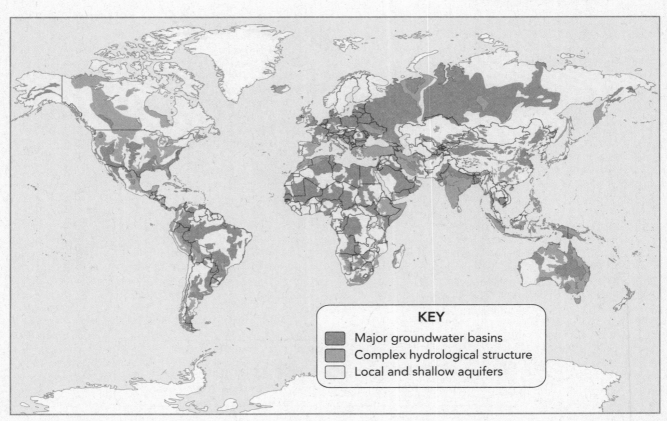

KEY
- Major groundwater basins
- Complex hydrological structure
- Local and shallow aquifers

Water Scarcity

Figure 4 Many people and regions will be affected by water scarcity in the future.

CCC Cause and Effect How might water scarcity affect economic development in an area?

....

....

....

....

Human Impacts

Humans rely on water not only to live and grow, but also for agriculture and industry. Water is needed to produce our food, manufacture products, and carry out many chemical reactions. The distribution of water resources is a result of past and current geologic processes such as the water cycle, plate tectonics, and the formation of rock. These processes take time, and in some areas humans are depleting water resources faster than they can be replenished. The human impact on water distribution is already a cause of social and economic conflict in some areas.

Using Water Humans use surface water, which often involves changing its natural path, such as with dams. This affects the amount of water that continues to flow and the ecology of the area. Humans access groundwater resources by digging wells in aquifers. But if more water is removed from an aquifer or other groundwater source than is replenished through the water cycle, water shortages can occur, such as the drought that affected California from 2011 through 2016. As with surface water, pollution can enter groundwater supplies and impact the quality of the water. Study the effects of water scarcity in **Figure 4**.

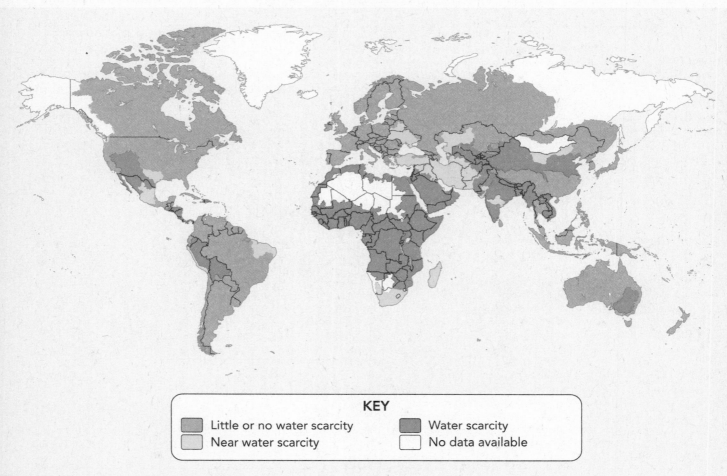

KEY

Little or no water scarcity

Near water scarcity

Water scarcity

No data available

Using Ocean Resources

Figure 5 If too many of these fish are caught, then fewer will survive to produce new generations.

Desalination

In the future, humans may look to technology and the ocean to meet their water needs. The process of desalination removes salt and minerals from saltwater to make fresh water. Today, **desalination** plants around the world are costly and require a lot of energy to distill saltwater. We may eventually use solar energy to convert ocean water into fresh water.

Other Water Resources

Humans rely on the ocean to provide a number of other important resources besides water, such as sea organisms for food and other products **(Figure 5)**. The ocean also provides salt, minerals, and fuels.

Living resources such as fish are replenished through natural cycles. However, overfishing can result in severe reductions or collapses of ocean ecosystems and the resources they provide. In addition, pollution and global climate change can have serious impacts on the biosphere resources we rely on from the ocean as well as freshwater ecosystems.

INTERACTIVITY

Examine the factors that affect water availability on Earth.

CHECK POINT

Identify What are some other ocean resources humans use besides water?

....

....

....

....

....

....

Design It!

Sustainable Fishing

Fish populations are replenished only if sufficient numbers are allowed to live and reproduce in their ecosystems.

SEP Design Solutions
Develop a design for a sustainable fishing net. Your net should function to allow only some fish to be caught, leaving others to replenish populations each year. Sketch your design in the space provided and label your sketch to explain how the net allows for sustainable fishing.

☑ LESSON 3 Check

MS-ESS3-1, EP&CIc

1. **Identify** What are the different sources of fresh water on Earth?

....
....
....
....
....
....

2. **SEP Construct Explanations** What factors account for the uneven distribution of groundwater on Earth?

....
....
....
....
....
....
....

3. **Infer** How could the release of human waste above an aquifer affect the health of that population?

....
....
....
....
....
....
....

4. **CCC Cause and Effect** Explain why some regions are more extremely affected by water scarcity than others.

....
....
....
....
....
....
....
....
....
....
....

5. **Connect to Society** In what way does water scarcity harm the economic development of an area?

....
....
....
....
....
....
....
....
....
....

Managing California's
Water Resources

The following excerpt is from the beginning of the Sustainable Groundwater Management Act, passed by the California legislature and signed by the governor in 2014.

(a) The Legislature finds and declares as follows:

(1) *The people of the state have a primary interest in the protection, management, and reasonable beneficial use of the water resources of the state, both surface and underground, and that the integrated management of the state's water resources is essential to meeting its water management goals.*

(2) *Groundwater provides a significant portion of California's water supply. Groundwater accounts for more than one-third of the water used by Californians in an average year and more than one-half of the water used by Californians in a drought year when other sources are unavailable.*

(3) *Excessive groundwater extraction can cause overdraft, failed wells, deteriorated water quality, environmental damage, and irreversible land subsidence that damages infrastructure and diminishes the capacity of aquifers to store water for the future.*

(4) *When properly managed, groundwater resources will help protect communities, farms, and the environment against prolonged dry periods and climate change, preserving water supplies for existing and potential beneficial use.*

(5) *Failure to manage groundwater to prevent long-term overdraft infringes on groundwater rights.*

(6) *Groundwater resources are most effectively managed at the local or regional level.*

CONNECT TO YOU

Find out more about California's water supply and the Sustainable Groundwater Management Act. As you research, consider these questions: How much water do Californians use? What are the sources for the state's water supply? What is the state doing to ensure that Californians have access to clean, safe water?

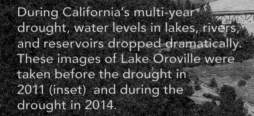

During California's multi-year drought, water levels in lakes, rivers, and reservoirs dropped dramatically. These images of Lake Oroville were taken before the drought in 2011 (inset) and during the drought in 2014.

MS-ESS3-1

Evidence-Based Assessment

Van is researching information about the mineral copper and its distribution on Earth. Copper is used in electrical systems and even found in very small amounts in living things. Here is some of the other information Van finds, along with two maps that he finds during his research:

- copper ore can form from different geological processes

- one type of copper, called porphyry copper, is found in large deposits in certain types of rock

- most porphyry copper deposits are 340 million years old or younger

- porphyry copper forms at relatively shallow depths of about 4,500 to 9,000 meters (15,000 to 30,000 feet) in Earth's crust

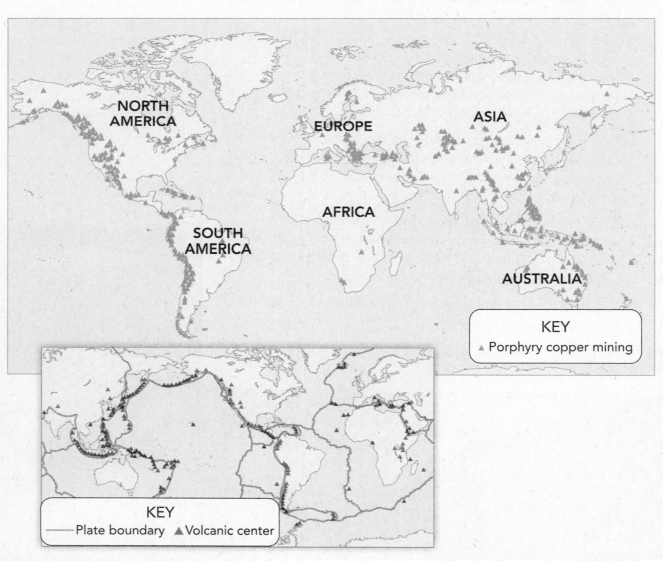

KEY
▲ Porphyry copper mining

KEY
—— Plate boundary ▲ Volcanic center

1. **SEP Analyze Data** Which of these regions seems to have the greatest concentration of porphyry copper mining?
   A. Africa   B. Australia
   C. Europe   D. South America

2. **CCC Cause and Effect** Why are there so many volcanoes around the Pacific Ocean? Select the correct answers to complete the following sentences.

   Most volcanic activity occurs along _____ .
   A. faults
   B. plate boundaries
   C. mountains

   This usually happens when _____ .
   A. two plates meet and one slides under the other
   B. two plates meet and crash into each other
   C. two continents meet underwater

3. **CCC Patterns** Based on the map of porphyry copper mining, which of the following statements about the distribution of copper is correct? Select all that apply.

   ☐ Porphyry copper is distributed relatively evenly across most of the continents.

   ☐ Very little porphyry copper is found in Africa.

   ☐ A concentration of porphyry copper runs from Europe eastward through Asia and then south into Australia.

   ☐ Porphyry copper is widely distributed across South America.

   ☐ A majority of porphyry copper is found on continents that border the Pacific Ocean.

   ☐ There are fewer sources of porphyry copper in North America than in Asia.

4. **SEP Construct Explanations** Use evidence from the maps to explain why porphyry copper is generally found near areas where volcanic activity, often associated with plate collisions, has occurred in the past.

   _____
   _____
   _____
   _____
   _____
   _____
   _____
   _____
   _____
   _____
   _____
   _____
   _____
   _____
   _____
   _____
   _____
   _____

To Drill or Not to Drill

How can you **use a model** to confirm the location of a **petroleum** deposit?

Materials

(per group)

- aquarium gravel
- glass baking dish
- wax crayons or candles
- plastic knife
- small weight or heavy book
- hot plate

Safety

Be sure to follow all safety guidelines provided by your teacher. The Safety Appendix of your textbook provides more details about the safety icons.

Background

Phenomenon An energy company wants to drill for oil on the outskirts of a small town. The owners of the energy company have provided evidence that the town is located near an area that was a large sea millions of years ago. Based on that evidence, they believe there is a large deposit of petroleum under the town. Town officials have hired you as an expert to look for evidence of oil under the town.

In this investigation, you will develop a model that you can use to predict whether or not the company will locate any oil below the town.

Develop Your Model

☐ 1. Using the available materials, your group must develop a model that meets the following criteria:

- It must show how oil forms from ancient marine organisms.

- It must demonstrate the geological forces involved in the formation of oil.

- It must indicate whether or not oil can form below the town.

☐ 2. Work with your group to develop ideas for a model that meets the criteria. Consider the following questions as you develop and design your model:

- What materials can you use to represent the buried organic material that eventually forms oil?

- How can your model demonstrate the geological forces that form oil?

- What observations will you make?

☐ 3. After agreeing on a plan, write out the steps that your group will follow to develop and use the model. Include a sketch of the model that labels the materials you will be using and what they represent.

☐ 4. After getting your teacher's approval, construct your model and use it to demonstrate how oil forms. Record your observations and data in the space provided.

uDemonstrate Lab

Plan and Sketch

Observations

....

....

....

....

....

....

....

....

....

....

....

....

....

....

....

Analyze and Interpret Data

1. **SEP Use Models** Use your model to explain why oil is a nonrenewable resource.

   ....

   ....

   ....

   ....

2. **CCC Cause and Effect** What geological forces are involved in the formation of oil? How did you incorporate these forces into your model?

   ....

   ....

   ....

   ....

   ....

3. **SEP Construct Explanations** Explain whether or not oil will be found under the town. Use evidence from your model to support your explanation.

   ....

   ....

   ....

   ....

   ....

   ....

4. **Identify Limitations** In what ways is your model not reflective of the actual conditions that lead to the formation of oil? How could your group improve the model?

   ....

   ....

   ....

   ....

   ....

   ....

Human Impacts on the Environment

Investigative Phenomenon
What actions can we take to reduce
our impact on Earth's systems?

MS-ESS3-4 Construct an argument supported by evidence for how increases in human population and per-capita consumption of natural resources impact Earth's systems.

MS-ETS1-4 Develop a model to generate data for iterative testing and modification of a proposed object, tool, or process such that an optimal design can be achieved.

EP&CIa Students should be developing an understanding that the goods produced by natural systems are essential to human life and to the functioning of our economies and cultures.

EP&CIb Students should be developing an understanding that the ecosystem services provided by natural systems are essential to human life and to the functioning of our economies and cultures.

EP&CIc Students should be developing an understanding that the quality, quantity, and reliability of the goods and ecosystem services provided by natural systems are directly affected by the health of those systems.

EP&CIIa Students should be developing an understanding that direct and indirect changes to natural systems due to the growth of human populations and their consumption rates influence the geographic extent, composition, biological diversity, and viability of natural systems.

EP&CIIb Students should be developing an understanding that methods used to extract, harvest, transport, and consume natural resources influence the geographic extent, composition, biological diversity, and viability of natural systems.

EP&CIIc Students should be developing an understanding that the expansion and operation of human communities influences the geographic extent, composition, biological diversity, and viability of natural systems

EP&CIIIc Students should be developing an understanding that human practices can alter the cycles and processes that operate within natural systems

EP&CIVa Students should be developing an understanding that the effects of human activities on natural systems are directly related to the quantities of resources consumed and to the quantity and characteristics of the resulting byproducts.

EP&CIVb Students should be developing an understanding that the byproducts of human activity are not readily prevented from entering natural systems and may be beneficial, neutral, or detrimental in their effect.

EP&CIVc Students should be developing an understanding that the capacity of natural systems to adjust to human-caused alterations depends on the nature of the system as well as the scope, scale, and duration of the activity and the nature of its byproducts.

EP&CVa Students should be developing an understanding of the spectrum of what is considered in making decisions about resources and natural systems and how those factors influence decisions.

What is happening to these trees?

HANDS-ON LAB

uConnect Explore ways that you can reduce the pollution you create.

What questions do you have about the phenomenon?

_____

_____

_____

_____

_____

_____

_____

_____

Quest PBL

How can you help your school reduce its impact on Earth's systems?

STEM ▶ **Figure It Out** The landfill used by your community is running out of space. The community must expand it or find other ways to deal with the trash. Your principal has decided to help the community by finding ways to reduce the school's trash output. In this problem-based Quest activity, you will evaluate the trash output at your school. You will then develop a plan to decrease that output through a combination of reducing, reusing, and recycling. As you work, you should anticipate objections to your plan. Finally, you will present your plan and work to implement it at your school.

NBC LEARN ▶ VIDEO

After watching the Quest Kickoff video, which explores the plastic items that end up in the ocean, think about the trash you generate. How can you reduce, recycle, or reuse your trash?

Reduce:

....

....

Recycle:

....

....

Reuse:

....

....

 INTERACTIVITY

Trash Backlash

 MS-ESS3-4

Quest CHECK-IN

IN LESSON 1

STEM ▶ How does the rate of trash generation affect landfills? Investigate how much trash is generated in an area of your school, and design and construct landfill models.

 INTERACTIVITY

More Trash, Less Space

Quest CHECK-IN

IN LESSON 2

How can landfills be constructed so they don't contaminate groundwater? Investigate how different designs will protect the water supply.

HANDS-ON LAB

Trash vs. Water

Quest CHECK-IN

IN LESSON 3

How is a landfill site chosen, and what laws regulate landfill use? Explore the stages of a landfill's life, and conduct research about laws that affect landfills.

 INTERACTIVITY

Life of a Landfill

According to the U.S. Environmental Protection Agency, Americans recycled only about 35 percent of their waste in 2014. Much of the rest of the waste ended up in landfills such as this one in Livermore, California.

Quest CHECK-IN

IN LESSON 4

How can everyone contribute to reducing waste at your school? Develop a plan to reduce trash output in at least one area of your school.

HANDS-ON LAB

Reducing Waste

Quest FINDINGS

Complete the Quest!

Refine and present your plan to reduce trash output at your school.

INTERACTIVITY

Reflect on Trash Backlash

LESSON

Population Growth and Resource Consumption

HANDS-ON LAB

Investigate Examine how population growth affects the availability of natural resources.

 MS-ESS3-4 Construct an argument supported by evidence for how increases in human population and per-capita consumption of natural resources impact Earth's systems.

Connect It!

✏️ **Draw a line to indicate where you think the city limits of Los Angeles were about 100 years ago.**

Apply Scientific Reasoning How do you think the amount of resources used by the human population of Los Angeles has changed in the past 100 years?

....

....

....

The Human Population

There are more humans living on Earth today than any time in our history. Human populations have fluctuated in the past, mostly due to environmental or climate conditions. Around 60,000 years ago, the human population was generally stable at around 600,000 individuals. A warming climate and improvements in hunting and fishing techniques resulted in a rapid increase to about 6 million humans over a few thousand years.

This population remained fairly constant until about 10,000 years ago, when agriculture and livestock breeding gave rise to steady, long-term population growth. This growth dropped occasionally during war, epidemics, or invasions, but maintained a steady climb until the 1700s. Since then, unprecedented population growth has occurred, with the human population reaching 1 billion by the early 1800s. In the last 300 years, the world population has increased tenfold. As of 2017, there were 7.5 billion people on Earth.

HANDS-ON LAB

Explore how food becomes a limiting factor when population size increases.

Reflect How has the population of your community changed in your lifetime? In your science notebook, describe some ways your community would be affected if the population were to suddenly increase or decrease.

Growth of a City

Figure 1 A little over 4 million people call the city of Los Angeles, California, home. The population has grown a great deal since the first Native American tribes settled there thousands of years ago.

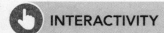
Academic Vocabulary

What other kinds of information might scientists need to estimate?

....

....

....

....

....

Population Changes

Population growth is determined by calculating the number of individuals who are born, die, or move into or out of an area. The number of births per 1,000 individuals for a certain time period is called the **birth rate**. On the other hand, the number of deaths per 1,000 individuals for a certain time period is called the **death rate**. When the rates of births and people moving into an area are greater than the rates of deaths and people moving out of an area, the population increases. Otherwise, the population decreases. In 2016, scientists **estimate** there were 280 births and 109 deaths every minute.

In early human history, birth rates and death rates were fairly balanced, which resulted in little change in the size of the human population. For most of human history, birth rates were only slightly higher than death rates, resulting in a slow, steady increase in population.

The graph in **Figure 2** shows human population growth beginning in 1750, around the start of the Industrial Revolution. Human population grew rapidly after the Industrial Revolution because the death rate began to decline. Advances in technology resulted in new farming and transportation methods that increased the availability of resources, such as food and clean water. Improvements in public health and general living standards also played a role in decreasing the death rate.

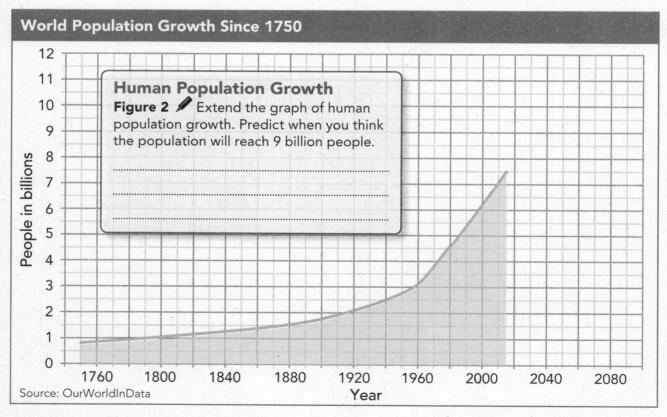

World Population Growth Since 1750

Human Population Growth

Figure 2 Extend the graph of human population growth. Predict when you think the population will reach 9 billion people.

....

....

....

Source: OurWorldInData

Population Growth Rate

Human population changes do not represent a straight line of increase on a graph. Instead the population increases more and more rapidly over time. This rate of change is called **exponential growth**—a growth pattern in which individuals in a population reproduce at a constant rate, so that the larger population gets, the faster it grows.

However, no living population can experience such extreme exponential growth for very long. Populations are limited by space and resources. Exponential growth will cease when a population reaches the upper limit of organisms its environment can support. At that point, the population will stabilize or possibly decline. Throughout history, human populations have experienced periods of growth and decline, depending on the conditions and resources available.

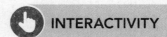
INTERACTIVITY

Learn about how human population growth affects Earth's systems.

✓ CHECK POINT **Determine Conclusions** What would happen if the population growth rate reached zero?

....

....

Math Toolbox

Projected Growth Rates

The rate of human population growth is not the same all around the world. Experts use existing data to predict growth rates in different countries. Some areas may experience rapid growth, while others may have no growth or a decline.

1. **SEP Interpret Data** Which country represented has the highest population growth rate? Lowest?

....

....

2. **SEP Evaluate Evidence** What conclusions can you draw from the growth rates of Angola and Germany?

....

....

....

....

Country	Population Growth Rate (%)
Angola	1.9
Australia	1.0
Canada	0.7
Germany	−0.2
Haiti	1.3
Japan	−0.2
South Korea	0.5
United States	0.8
Venezuela	1.2

Source: CIA World Factbook, 2017 estimates

uInvestigate Examine how population growth affects the availability of natural resources.

Academic Vocabulary

What are some other words that have the same meaning as *constraint*?

....

....

....

Using Natural Resources

Earth provides many resources that humans rely on to live, such as energy sources, minerals, water, trees, and plants. These resources are needed by all organisms on Earth. Some resources, such as water, are part of systems that affect our planet's climate and other natural cycles.

Human Activity Industries and families alike rely on energy sources such as fossil fuels to provide electricity to power our lives. We use fuel to keep us warm in the winter and cool in the summer, to travel from place to place, and to grow and transport the food we eat. We use wood from trees and minerals that are mined from the ground to build everything from the tiniest computer chips to the tallest skyscrapers. Every human being relies on fresh, clean water to survive.

As the world's population grows, so does our demand for resources. Like the human population, many resources are not evenly distributed around Earth. For example, the availability of fresh, usable water varies in different locations on Earth. It is one of the factors that may act as a **constraint** on human activities in the near future. Currently, more than 700 million people do not have access to safe, clean water. This lack of clean water forces many individuals to consume unsafe water. Experts estimate that by 2025, nearly 1.8 billion people could be suffering from water scarcity.

Question It !

Mining Salt

Salt is not only a necessary part of the human diet, it is used in numerous industrial and agricultural applications. Most of the salt used today is mined from underground deposits.

SEP Ask Questions Develop a list of questions you would ask to help determine the relationship between human population growth and salt mining.

Impact of Agriculture
Figure 3 In order to grow food for people to eat, farmers use fertilizers and other chemicals. These chemicals often run off the land and pollute lakes, rivers, and the ocean.
CCC Cause and Effect What effect does farming food for a growing population have on the environment?

....
....
....
....
....
....

Impact on the Earth System The use of natural resources has both short and long-term consequences, positive and negative, for the health of people and for the natural environment. We need natural resources. But using resources reduces the amount of nonrenewable resources like fossil fuels. Also, obtaining many of these resources involves drilling, mining, or clearing Earth's surface, which damages the land. As some resources such as minerals or fossil fuels become scarce, humans dig deeper and disturb more areas to keep up with our growing population. Human consumption, or use, of resources creates waste. Untreated waste can harm the environment. Motorized vehicles burn petroleum and release chemicals that can cause **pollution**, the contamination of Earth's land, water, or air.

Human activities also affect other life on Earth. When we mine for a mineral or divert water for agriculture (**Figure 3**) we often destroy valuable habitats. Pollution in land and water habitats endangers the organisms that live there. Also, many organisms are over-exploited as food. When the number of humans grows beyond what the available resources can support, we reach the point of **overpopulation**. Human overpopulation and rising per-capita (per person) consumption of natural resources contribute to many environmental and social issues, including climate change, habitat loss, and human conflict. There may come a point at which Earth cannot adequately meet human needs at our current rate of resource use.

Literacy Connection

Determine Conclusions As you read, underline evidence in the text that supports your conclusions about how growing populations impact the environment.

☑ CHECK POINT **Determine Conclusions** How does a growing population impact land, air, and water resources?

....

....

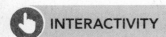
Balancing Needs

Science can identify problems and offer possible solutions, but it is up to individuals, governments, and international organizations to decide how to manage the impacts of a growing population. There are economic, social, and environmental costs and benefits which all must be weighed against one another (**Figure 4**). For example, humans use a variety of resources to produce electricity, from burning fossil fuels to building dams. No single method works in every situation, and there are benefits and costs to each.

The practice of using less of a resource so that it can last longer is called **conservation**. To ensure that future generations have access to the same resources we enjoy now, we need to use resources in ways that maintain them at a certain quality for a certain period of time. This practice is known as **sustainable use** of living resources. It gives resources time to recover and replenish themselves.

Harvesting Timber

Figure 4 We use timber, but there is an impact of our use on the environment. In the table, list the benefits and costs of logging.

Addressing human impacts on the environment also requires engineering new solutions to our problems. These might include using desalination to counter water shortages, or advances in solar power, wind power, and other forms of renewable energy. As human populations continue to rise, the need for new ideas and solutions will increase.

☑ CHECK POINT **Develop an Argument** Why is it important to conserve natural resources?

....

....

....

Benefits	Costs

☑ LESSON 1 Check

MS-ESS3-4

1. SEP Cite Evidence What factors limited human population growth in the past?

....

....

....

....

2. CCC Cause and Effect How did the Industrial Revolution affect human population growth?

....

....

....

....

....

3. SEP Engage in Argument What actions should humans take to conserve natural resources?

....

....

....

....

....

Use the graph to answer questions 4 and 5.

Human Population 1750–2020

4. CCC Evaluate Proportions What was the approximate population growth per year from 1800 to 1925? What was the approximate growth rate from 1925 to 2000? What is the ratio between the two rates?

....

....

....

5. Use Ratios Suggest two explanations for the ratio relationship you described in question 4.

....

....

....

Quest CHECK-IN

In this lesson, you learned how human population has changed over time and how human population growth impacts Earth's systems.

Connect to the Environment Why is it important to consider human population growth when developing strategies for dealing with pollution?

....

....

....

....

INTERACTIVITY

More Trash, Less Space

Go online to learn about the total volume of trash generated in the United States and to determine how much trash is generated at your school.

2 Air Pollution

HANDS-ON LAB

uInvestigate Evaluate how different types of pollution affect air and water clarity.

MS-ESS3-4 Construct an argument supported by evidence for how increases in human population and per-capita consumption of natural resources impact Earth's systems.

Connect It !

✏️ **Circle each mode of transportation that causes air pollution.**

SEP Construct Explanations How do these different forms of transportation pollute the air?

....

....

Make Predictions What is the benefit of walking or riding a bike?

....

....

Causes of Pollution

You are surrounded by air. Air is a mixture of nitrogen, oxygen, carbon dioxide, water vapor, and other gases. Almost all living things depend on these gases to survive. These gases cycle between the biosphere and the atmosphere. The cycles guarantee that the air supply will not run out, but they don't ensure that the air will be clean.

Pollution The contamination of Earth's land, water, or air is called pollution. Pollution is caused by liquids, chemicals, heat, light, and noise. Pollution can have short-term and long-term negative consequences on the environment and on the health of living organisms, including people.

Humans affect the levels of pollution by using natural resources and manufactured products. For example, **Figure 1** shows how the burning of gasoline pollutes the air. In addition, when coal and oil-based fuels are burned to generate electricity, carbon dioxide and sulfur dioxide are released into the air.

Types of Pollution A specific, identifiable pollution source is called a **point source**. A sewer that drains untreated wastewater into a river is an example of a point source.

A **nonpoint source** of pollution is widely spread and cannot be tied to a specific origin. For example, the polluted air around big cities is caused by vehicles, factories, and other sources. Because it is difficult to identify the exact source of the pollution, that pollution has a nonpoint source.

✓ CHECK POINT **Determine Central Ideas** What is the difference between point and nonpoint sources of pollution?

....

....

....

HANDS-ON LAB

Explore how particles move through the air.

Reflect What might be some short-term and long-term impacts of breathing polluted air?

Different Sources of Pollution

Figure 1 Pollution can occur naturally or through human activities. Sometimes the level of pollution is so great that it harms people.

Forest fires

Industrial emissions

Motor vehicle emissions

Livestock

Sources of Air Pollution

Figure 2 ✏ Circle the natural sources of pollution. Mark an X on the human-made causes of pollution.

HANDS-ON LAB

Investigate Evaluate how different types of pollution affect air and water clarity.

Outdoor Air Pollution

The air you are breathing is a combination of different gases. If you are in the mountains, the air might feel fresh and crisp. If you are at the shore, you might smell the salt water. In large cities, however, the air might not be as refreshing. Air pollution can be a big problem in areas where there are a lot of factories or a lot of people.

Emissions Many years ago, the main source of air pollution was the smoke being pumped out of factories. You have probably seen images of these **emissions**, or pollutants that are released into the air, as the dark smoke coming out of a factory's tall chimneys. This smoke is loaded with chemicals that mix with the gases in the air. However, today, most air pollution is released from coal-fired power plants and from motor vehicles, as shown in **Figure 2**. Emissions often contain carbon dioxide, which is also a pollutant. The increasing level of carbon dioxide is the primary contributor to the rise in average global temperatures over the past century.

Not all air pollution is caused by people. There are also some natural causes of air pollution, such as forest fires and volcanic eruptions. For example, the Hawaiian volcano Kilauea releases nearly 1,500–2,000 tons of harmful sulfur dioxide into the atmosphere each day during eruptions. However, human activities emit more than ten times as much sulfur dioxide and more than one hundred times as much carbon dioxide as all volcanoes combined.

Smog

If you live in a large city, chances are you have heard the term "smog alert." This is a warning to alert you that the amount of air pollution may make it difficult to breathe outdoors. Smog forms when certain gases and chemicals react with sunlight. This results in a thick, brownish haze that hovers over a city. Smog can cause breathing problems and diseases of the eyes and throat.

The **primary** source of smog is the emissions of cars and trucks. Among these emissions are chemicals called hydrocarbons and nitrogen oxides. These gases react in the sunlight to produce a form of oxygen called **ozone**. Ozone is toxic to humans, and it causes lung infections and harms the body's immune system.

Under normal conditions, air near the ground is heated by Earth's surface and rises up and away from the surface. Pollutants in the air are carried up into the atmosphere by the rising air. However, under certain weather conditions called temperature inversions, the normal circulation of air is blocked. As **Figure 3** shows, cool air becomes trapped below a layer of warm air during an inversion. This keeps the pollutants trapped near Earth's surface and causes them to become more concentrated and dangerous.

✓ CHECK POINT **Cite Textual Evidence** What are the main sources of air pollution and how do they cause smog?

....

....

....

Academic Vocabulary
Write a sentence using the word *primary*.

....

....

....

Temperature Inversion
Figure 3 ✏ Complete the image on the right by shading in the air pollutants to show how they are trapped during a temperature inversion.

Normal conditions

Cold Air

Cool Air

Warm Air

Temperature inversion

Cold Air

Warm Air

Cool Air

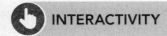
Acid Rain

Acid Rain Precipitation that is more acidic than normal because of air pollution is called **acid rain**. When coal and oil are burned, they produce nitrogen oxide and sulfur dioxide gases. These gases are then released as emissions and react with the water vapor in the air to produce nitric and sulfuric acids. These acids become part of rain, snow, sleet, or fog.

When acidic precipitation falls to Earth's surface, it has damaging effects, as shown in **Figure 4**. As water and soil become more acidic, organisms will die off. Acid rain can also remove nutrients and minerals from the soil, affecting plant growth. Sometimes the effects of acid rain can be reversed by adding chemicals that neutralize the acid, but this is very expensive.

Acid rain also causes damage to nonliving things. The acid reacts with metal and stone of buildings, cars, and statues. It can cause metal to rust at a faster rate and causes the chemical weathering of stone. The effects of acid rain on these materials are irreversible.

Literacy Connection

Cite Textual Evidence
As you read, underline the statements that support the idea that acid rain causes damage to living and nonliving things.

☑ **CHECK POINT** **Write Arguments** Suppose your town government does not think that outdoor air pollution is a problem. What evidence could you use to convince the local government that air pollution is harmful to people and the environment?

....

....

....

....

....

Effects of Acid Rain

Figure 4 Acid rain can damage nonliving things as well as living things. Explain how acid rain might affect the trees in a forest.

....

....

....

....

....

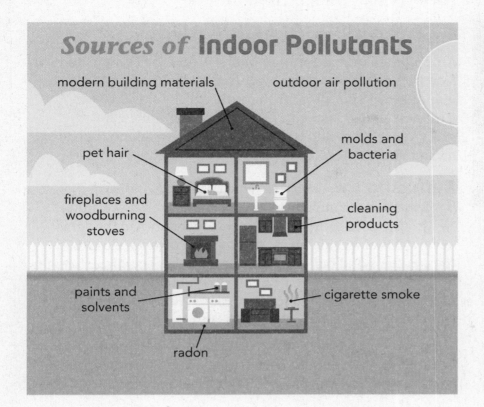

Sources of Indoor Pollutants

modern building materials

outdoor air pollution

pet hair

molds and bacteria

fireplaces and woodburning stoves

cleaning products

paints and solvents

cigarette smoke

radon

Indoor Air Pollution
Figure 5 Underline the indoor pollutants that are human-made. Circle the pollutants that occur naturally.

Indoor Air Pollution

Sometimes the quality of the air inside a building can be just as bad as the air outside. There are several things that can contribute to indoor air pollution, as shown in **Figure 5**. Some of these can be human-made, while others occur naturally.

Allergens Obvious sources of indoor air pollution include dust, mold, and pet hair. These factors, while quite common, usually affect only people who are sensitive to them. Other sources of indoor air pollution include fumes from glues, paints, and cleaning supplies and tobacco smoke from cigarettes or cigars. These can affect everyone in the home.

Indoor Gases Radon and carbon monoxide are two harmful pollutants often found in homes or other buildings. Radon is a colorless, odorless gas that is radioactive. It forms underground from the decay of certain rocks. Radon enters a home through cracks in the foundation. Breathing this gas over long periods of time can cause lung cancer and other health issues.

Carbon monoxide forms when fuels such as oil, gas, or wood are burned. Breathing carbon monoxide causes respiratory issues, nausea, headaches, and even death.

The best way to protect against carbon monoxide is to install detectors near sleeping areas. These devices alert homeowners if concentrations get too high.

VIDEO

Explore the misconception that indoor spaces do not suffer from air pollution.

CHECK POINT
Integrate With Visuals
What are some ways to reduce the amount of indoor pollution in your home?

....
....
....
....
....
....
....
....
....

Controlling Air Pollution

Air pollution affects weather patterns and the climate and can lead to illness and death. According to one recent study, air pollution is responsible for the early deaths of more than 5 million people, including 200,000 in the United States every year. California is at the forefront of working to reduce air pollution.

Reducing Emissions The automobile industry implemented technology to lower emissions in new vehicles. Newer fuel-efficient vehicles use less fuel to travel the same distance as older models. Scientists have also developed cleaner fuels and biofuels that release fewer chemicals into the air. Electric or hybrid vehicles use a combination of electricity and gasoline, which reduces emissions. Some all-electric vehicles produce zero emissions.

Other ways to reduce emissions include carpooling, biking, or walking. You can also avoid using gas-powered lawn and garden tools and buy only energy-efficient appliances.

Changing Energy Usage Another way to reduce emissions is to transition away from fossil fuels, such as coal, oil, and natural gas. Solar, wind, hydroelectric, and geothermal energy produce only a small fraction of the harmful emissions that the burning of fossil fuels generates.

Bike Sharing

Figure 6 Bike-sharing programs, found in many major California cities, provide a clean-energy alternative to driving a car or taking a bus. What actions can you take to reduce air pollution in your community?

....

....

....

Math Toolbox

Energy Usage

The graphs show how energy consumption has changed in the United States over the past century.

1. **Use Ratios** How many times greater was energy consumption in 1908 than in 2015?

....

2. **Analyze Quantitative Relationships** Describe any patterns you observe in the graph showing the proportion of consumption for each energy source. What do you think might explain these patterns?

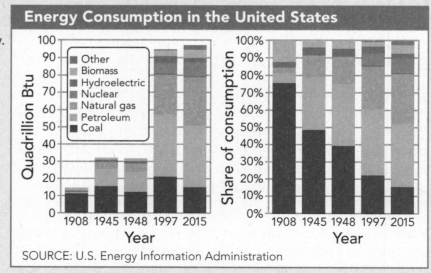

Energy Consumption in the United States

SOURCE: U.S. Energy Information Administration

....

....

Protecting the Ozone Layer

If you have ever been sunburned, then you have experienced the effects of the sun's ultraviolet, or UV, radiation. The ozone layer, situated about 15 to 30 km above Earth's surface, works like a shield to protect living things from too much UV radiation.

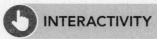
INTERACTIVITY

Explore how to reduce your carbon footprint.

The Ozone Cycle

In the ozone layer, ozone is constantly being made and destroyed in a cycle. An ozone molecule has three oxygen atoms. When sunlight hits a molecule, the ozone absorbs UV radiation. The energy causes the ozone to break apart into an oxygen gas molecule (which has two oxygen atoms) and a single oxygen atom. The oxygen atom hits an oxygen molecule and attaches itself to form a new ozone molecule.

The Ozone Hole

In the late 1970s, scientists discovered an area of severe ozone depletion, or a "hole," in the ozone layer over the southern polar region, shown in **Figure 7**. The main cause of the hole was a group of gases called chlorofluorocarbons (CFCs)—human-made gases that destroy ozone molecules. As a result, more UV radiation reached Earth's surface. Nations around the world worked together to ban CFCs to help restore the amount of ozone in the atmosphere.

☑ CHECK POINT **Determine Conclusions** Why did countries work together to ban CFCs to help restore the ozone layer?

....

....

....

....

Ozone Hole

Figure 7 A hole in the ozone layer (in blue) allows more harmful UV radiation to reach Earth's surface in the Southern Hemisphere.

Model It!

Ozone Model

Re-read the paragraph about the ozone cycle.

SEP **Develop Models** ✏ Use the information in the text to create and label a model of an ozone molecule and how it changes during its life cycle. Explain each stage of the cycle.

....

....

....

....

....

MS-ESS3-4

1. **Determine Differences** What is the difference between "helpful" and "harmful" ozone?

....

....

....

....

2. **Evaluate Reasoning** Why is the use of fertilizers on lawns in residential areas an example of a nonpoint source of pollution?

....

....

....

3. **SEP Provide Evidence** How does burning fossil fuels affect indoor air pollution?

....

....

....

....

....

4. **CCC Cause and Effect** What effect does burning fossil fuels during manufacturing and energy production have on outdoor air pollution?

....

....

....

....

....

....

....

5. **Construct an Argument** What evidence supports the claim that walking and biking to work would have a positive effect on air pollution?

....

....

....

....

....

Quest CHECK-IN

In this lesson, you learned how humans affect Earth's systems by producing different forms of air pollution. You also learned how we are working to reduce the impact of air pollution.

SEP Evaluate Evidence Why is it important to work toward reducing activities that contribute to air pollution?

....

....

....

....

....

....

HANDS-ON LAB

Trash vs. Water

Go online to download the lab to design and construct a model of a landfill.

MS-ESS3-4, EP&CIa, EP&CIb,
EP&CIc, EP&CIIa, EP&CIIb, EP&CIIc,
EP&CIVa, EP&CIVb, EP&CIVc, EP&CVa

Reducing
Climate Change
Together

Climate change is a global issue. Warming temperatures will change weather patterns, raise ocean levels, and rapidly change ecosystems worldwide. But solutions begin locally. The effects of changing climate include both short and long-term consequences. These include organisms that cannot adapt, and can therefore no longer provide food and ecosystem services for human communities. In 2015, Governor Brown of California issued an Executive Order to reduce greenhouse gas (GHG) emissions to 40% less than 1990 levels by 2030. California hopes to achieve that vision by reaching the following goals:

- Increase renewable electricity to 50%
- Double energy efficiency savings at existing buildings
- Reduce short-lived climate pollutants, such as: methane, soot, and hydrofluorocarbon propellants
- Reduce petroleum use by vehicles by 50%
- Reduce GHG emissions from land
- Safeguard California from droughts, floods, wildfires, and any negative impact that may result from climate change

California's state government is also working with other governmental agencies on a global level. Its Intergovernmental Working Group for the Climate Action Team coordinates and implements work with other states, countries, and areas interested in reducing air pollution and greenhouse gas emissions. Climate change is a global problem. It is important for local, state, and national governments to work together to develop and complete plans to reduce GHG emissions.

MY COMMUNITY

What are communities in California doing to reduce climate change? Explore the local tab of the California Climate Center website to find out.

The use of more hybrid and zero-emission vehicles, such as this electric bus, is essential to California reaching its 2030 greenhouse gas reduction goal.

ZERO EMISSION VEHICLE

3 Impacts on Land

Investigate Examine the impacts of mining.

MS-ESS3-4 Construct an argument supported by evidence for how increases in human population and per-capita consumption of natural resources impact Earth's systems.

Connect It!

✏ **Identify and label one renewable resource and one nonrenewable resource shown in the image.**

CCC Cause and Effect What impact do you think the overuse of certain resources might have on Earth's ecosystems?

....

....

Land as a Resource

Did you drink water, turn on a light, or ride in a bus today? All of these activities, and many more, depend on Earth's **resources**. Anything we use that occurs naturally in the environment is called a **natural resource**. As **Figure 1** shows, natural resources include organisms, water, sunlight, minerals, and soil.

A **renewable resource** is either always available or is naturally replaced in a relatively short time. Some renewable resources, such as wind and sunlight, are almost always available. Other renewable resources, such as water and trees, are renewable only if they are replaced as fast as they are used.

Nonrenewable resources are resources that are not replaced within a relatively short time frame. Metals and most minerals are nonrenewable. Oil and coal are also nonrenewable resources. Fossil fuels such as oil and coal form over millions of years from the remains of organisms. At the rate humans are using fossil fuels, over time, they will be used up soon. All human activity that involves resources has short and long-term consequences that can be either beneficial or harmful for the health of humans. Resource use always has harmful effects on the environment.

While it does not cover as much of the planet's surface as water, land is also a vital resource. Humans use its many resources to survive. As **Figure 2** will show, it is used to grow food, obtain raw materials, and provide shelter.

Academic Vocabulary
A resource is not limited to a material, such as water or trees. What other kinds of resources do you rely on in your life?

....

....

....

....

Reflect What are some renewable and nonrenewable resources that you use? In your science notebook, describe these resources.

Natural Resources
Figure 1 As this image of a windfarm in Los Angeles, California, illustrates, human activity draws on different types of natural resources, both renewable, such as wind, and nonrenewable, such as gasoline.

Agriculture Land provides most of the food people eat. The use of land to produce food is called agriculture. Many areas of the world are not suitable for farming. New farmland is often made by draining wetlands, irrigating deserts, or deforestation. **Deforestation** is the removal of forests to use the land for other reasons. This process destroys the habitats of organisms living in these places.

Mining The metals and plastics used to make items such as televisions, cellular phones, building materials, and cars are mined from below Earth's surface. Metals and other resources are obtained through a type of mining called strip mining. Strip mining removes the top layer of dirt, exposing the minerals or ore underneath. When heavy winds and rains come, they can wash soil and land away. With it go all the nutrients it contains. It can take thousands of years for soil to be replaced.

Development Where do you live? It is a good bet that you live in a structure somewhere on the land. Whether it is a house, a camper, or an apartment building, the space your home takes up was once a habitat for other organisms. As the human population grows, more and more land is developed and built up with human structures, changing the habitat and often forcing organisms to find habitat elsewhere.

☑ CHECK POINT

Cite Textual Evidence
Which statements from the text support the idea that land is an important resource? Underline them.

clear-cutting

strip mining

development

Land Use

Figure 2 Humans use land in many different ways. How do increases in human population impact Earth's systems?

....

....

....

....

Importance of Soil Management

Healthy, fertile soil is essential for the success of agriculture because it contains the minerals and nutrients that plants require. Soil absorbs, stores, and filters water, which is also necessary for plant growth. Organisms living in soil, such as bacteria, fungi, and earthworms, break down the wastes and remains of living things and return them to the soil as nutrients.

Structure of Soil If you take a shovel and dig a hole in the ground, you will encounter several layers of soil, such as those shown in **Figure 3**. The first layer is called the litter. This top layer is where dead leaves and grass are found.

The next layer is called the topsoil. Topsoil is a mixture of nutrients, water, air, rock fragments, and dead and decaying organisms. Moving further down, the shovel will hit the subsoil. This layer contains the same water and air as the topsoil, but there are more rock fragments and fewer plant and animal remains here.

Underneath the subsoil is the layer of bedrock. This is the layer that makes up Earth's crust and is the basis for new soil. As time passes, water dissolves the rock, and its freezing and thawing action cracks and breaks apart the bedrock. Plant roots also help to break the bedrock by growing into cracks and then expanding. Animals such as earthworms and moles also help in the process. And as dead organisms break down, their remains contribute to the mixture of new soil.

Soil Layers

Figure 3 🖉 Fertile soil is made up of several layers. Label each layer of soil in the photo: *bedrock, litter, subsoil, topsoil.*

Plan It!

Community Considerations

CCC Cause and Effect Suppose you are part of a group that is converting an abandoned lot into a community garden. You need to plan the garden to avoid damaging the local environment further. What harmful effects should you consider and how can you minimize them?

....

....

....

....

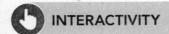

INTERACTIVITY

Explore how agriculture has affected soil and land.

Erosion Without soil, life on land could not exist. Soil takes hundreds of years to form. Therefore, every effort must be made to protect Earth's soil. Sometimes, natural forces cause soil loss. Forces such as wind, water, and ice move particles of rocks or soil through a process called **erosion**.

Usually, plant roots growing deep into the soil help to hold it in place. Human activities such as mining, logging, construction, and farming increase erosion by taking away these plants and exposing the soil to wind and precipitation. With nothing to anchor them in place, soil particles easily move. Human activities cause erosion to happen at a much faster rate than naturally-ocurring processes do. **Figure 4** shows some examples of natural and human-caused erosion.

Erosion

Figure 4 ✏ Check the image that shows naturally-ocurring erosion.

CCC Cause and Effect How did different events cause these areas to form?

....

....

....

....

....

....

....

....

Nutrient Depletion Plants make their own food through photosynthesis, but they need to take in nutrients such as nitrogen and phosphorus. Decomposers in the soil break down dead organisms, which add these and other nutrients to the soil. If a farmer plants the same crops in a field every year, the crops may use more nutrients than decomposers can supply. This leads to nutrient depletion; the soil is not adequately fertile. Nutrient depletion can directly affect humans. Crops grown in nutrient-poor soil often have less nutritional value.

Farmers add fertilizers to the soil to provide the needed nutrients. This can produce abundant, nutritious crops, but can also cause damage when rain carries the fertilizers into nearby bodies of water. Farmers often manage the soil by allowing it to sit for a season or two in between plantings. This allows the remnant crops to decompose, which replenishes the soil with nutrients.

Desertification When the soil in a once-fertile area loses its moisture and nutrients, the area can become a desert. The advance of desert-like conditions into areas that were previously fertile is called **desertification**.

One cause of moisture loss is drought. During these prolonged periods of low precipitation, plants, including crops, will dry up or not grow at all. Allowing livestock to overgraze grasslands and cutting down trees without replanting the area can also result in desertification. Without plant roots to hold the soil together, erosion of fertile topsoil will occur. Plant roots also carry water deeper into the soil, so it doesn't dry out as quickly.

From 2010 to 2016, the state of California experienced a severe drought. The people of California took preventive actions to avoid desertification. The state introduced mandatory water restrictions and regulations on the use of groundwater. Farmers also reduced the growing of certain crops to lessen the need for extensive irrigation.

☑ CHECK POINT **Translate Information** In addition to precipitation, what could help reverse the conditions in **Figure 5**?

....

....

....

Avoiding desertification

Figure 5 During California's most recent drought, strong leadership and cooperation of citizens helped prevent the spread of conditions like those seen here at the South Lake Reservoir near Bishop.

Math Toolbox

Causes of Land Degradation

Degraded land is in danger of desertification. Scientists estimate that there are at least 79.5 million hectares of degraded land in North America. The graph shows the causes.

Analyze Proportional Relationships How many more hectares were degraded by agricultural activities than by deforestation? Show your work.

....

....

....

....

....

....

Degraded Land in North America

7.7%   5.4%   52.1%

79.5 Million hectares

34.8%

- ■ Agricultural activities
- ■ Overgrazing
- ■ Overexploitation of vegetation for domestic use
- ■ Deforestation

SOURCE: United Nations Environment Programme

123

VIDEO

Learn more about what happens when you throw something "away."

Student Discourse
With a partner, discuss why it may be that capped landfills can be used for some purposes but not others.

Land Reclamation
Figure 6 ✏ These pictures show a mine that was reclaimed to include a stream. Add numbers to put these pictures in chronological order.

SEP Construct Explanations Explain what happened to the land in these pictures.

....

....

....

....

Landfills When you are asked to take out the garbage, where does it go once it leaves your curb? Today much of the solid waste, construction debris, and agricultural and industrial waste we produce is buried in holes called landfills. These areas are designed to protect the surrounding areas from soil and water pollution. If landfills are not managed correctly, they can harm the environment. Materials from waste can leak into the groundwater, making it toxic to drink.

Once a landfill is full, it is covered with soil heavy in clay to keep rainwater from entering the waste. These "capped" landfills can be reclaimed as locations for parks and sports arenas. Landfills take up large spaces that can never be used again for most human uses, including agriculture and housing.

Land Reclamation It is sometimes possible to restore soil that has been lost to erosion or mining. This process of restoring land to a more productive state is called land reclamation. Land reclamation could involve trucking in soil from another area. Sometimes mine operations reclaim land by storing the soil that they remove from a site, then putting it back after mining operations cease. Land reclamation can restore farming areas as well as wildlife habitats (see **Figure 6**). Land reclamation is very expensive and difficult. It is much harder to bring back damaged land than it is to protect and conserve those resources before they become damaged.

☑ **CHECK POINT** **Draw Evidence** How do human actions impact land? Give one positive and one negative impact.

....

....

....

Wetlands

A wetland is an area in which water covers the soil for all or most of the year. They are found in all climates and on all continents except Antarctica. Other terms you may have heard for wetland include bog, marsh, and swamp.

Figure 7 shows how wetlands support both land and aquatic ecosystems. They serve as breeding and nursery grounds for many organisms, provide habitats to many species of plants, and are feeding sites for many birds, mammals, and fish.

Human activities greatly impact wetlands. The development of homes, businesses, and roads requires controlling the flow of water through these areas. But altering the flow of water in a wetland changes the ecosystem and destroys unique habitats. It can also lead to increases in erosion, flooding, and the pollution of water and soil. Wetland soil acts as a natural "sponge" to collect water. Without wetlands, the large amounts of rain produced by severe storms, such as hurricanes, would flow directly into rivers or populated areas. Wetlands help to protect the quality of water by trapping excess sediments and pollutants before they reach the groundwater or waterways.

☑ CHECK POINT **Integrate With Visuals** How would filling in a wetland to create a field affect the surrounding environment?

....

....

....

Literacy Connection

Cite Textual Evidence
When you write an argument, it should be based on factual evidence, not opinions. As you read, underline the evidence that supports the idea that human activities negatively affect the land.

How Wetlands Work
Figure 7 🖊 Wetland plants, soil, and bacteria protect surrounding aspects. Circle the aspects of the wetland that provide benefits to humans.

plants filter out pollutants and sediments

dissipates stream energy

provides critical wildlife habitat

groundwater flow

bacteria break down pollutants

specialized roots stabilize soil

saturated soil stores water

Figure 8 Examine the forest closely. Notice the amount of deforestation.

SEP Engage in Argument Do you think these trees are being managed in a way that maintains the overall health of the forest? Explain.

....

....

....

....

....

....

....

....

Sustainable Forest Management

Trees and other plants, like the ones in **Figure 8**, are important land resources. They provide food and shelter for many organisms. Through photosynthesis, they release oxygen into the air. They also absorb carbon dioxide and other pollutants from the air. Their roots absorb rainwater and hold the soil together, which helps to prevent erosion and flooding.

Many products are made from the fruit, seeds, and other parts of forest plants. The wood from some trees is used for making paper, and other trees are used to build homes and furniture. Fruits and seeds from trees provide food for people and animals.

All trees, whether cultivated by farmers or growing in the wild, need to be protected and managed sustainably. Because we can plant trees to replace trees that are cut down, forests can be renewable resources. How long a resource lasts depends on how people use it. **Sustainable** use of a resource means using it in ways that maintain the resource for all future generations. Replacing and reserving trees are important ways to sustain a forest. These practices ensure that the ecosystem remains healthy and that people can still depend on forests for the resources they need.

Logging Methods There are two main methods of logging, or cutting down trees: clear-cutting and selective cutting, illustrated in **Figure 9**. Clear-cutting is the process of cutting down all the trees in an area at once. Selective cutting is the process of cutting down only some trees in a forest and leaving a mix of tree sizes and species behind.

Clear-cutting is usually faster and less expensive than selective cutting. However, selective cutting is less damaging to the forest ecosystem than clear-cutting. When a forest is cleared, all the animals' habitats are suddenly gone. Without the protection of the trees, the soil is more easily eroded by wind and rain. The soil can then be blown or washed away and into nearby streams, harming aquatic ecosystems.

Selective cutting takes much longer, as the loggers need to actively choose which trees will come down and which will remain. It is more dangerous for loggers to selectively cut trees because they have to move heavy equipment and logs around the remaining trees.

Logging Methods
Figure 9 🖉 Clear-cutting and selective cutting are two methods of tree harvesting. Label each method shown as clear-cutting or selective cutting.

Original Forest

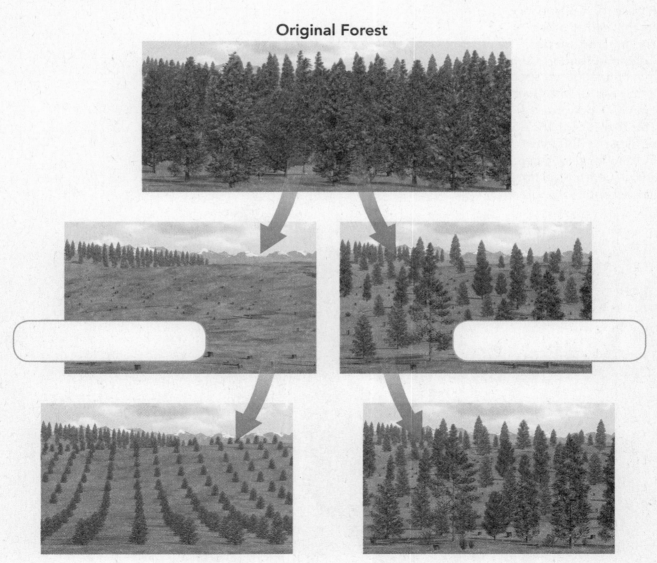

127

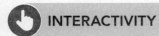
Write About It Collect information about how trees in your state are managed. In your science notebook, write an argument from the position of a conservation organization that says the yield is too high and needs to be reduced.

Conserving Forest Habitats

Figure 10 Conserving forests can also help endangered species. The California condor is the most endangered species in the world, with fewer than 450 individuals alive. This four-foot-tall, 25-pound bird can fly 100 miles a day looking for dead animals to scavenge from, so it needs large, continuous forests.

Sustainable Forestry Forests can be managed to provide a sustainable yield. A sustainable yield is the amount of a renewable resource that can be harvested regularly without reducing the future supply. Planting one tree to replace each one that is cut down ensures that the overall yield remains constant.

In sustainable forestry, after trees are harvested, young trees are planted, as shown in **Figure 10**. Trees must be planted frequently enough to maintain a constant supply. Forests containing fast-growing tree species, such as pines, can be harvested and replanted every 20 to 30 years. Forests containing slower-growing species, such as hickory, oak, and cherry, may be harvested only every 40 to 100 years. One sustainable approach is to log small patches within a forest, so different sections can be harvested every year.

☑ CHECK POINT **Draw Evidence** Why is it important to manage forests so that their yield is sustainable?

....

....

....

....

....

....

☑ LESSON 3 Check

 MS-ESS3-4

1. **Communicate** What are three different ways land is used as a resource?

....

....

2. **SEP Cite Evidence** Why are trees considered a renewable resource?

....

....

....

3. **Construct Arguments** How do poor farming methods impact Earth?

....

....

....

....

....

....

4. **SEP Evaluate Evidence** Give evidence to defend the claim that it is environmentally unsound to change the flow of water in a wetland.

....

....

....

....

....

....

....

5. **CCC Cause and Effect** How does the presence of trees maintain the stability of land resources?

....

....

....

....

....

Quest CHECK-IN

In this lesson, you learned about natural resources found on land and their importance to Earth's systems. You also learned how humans positively and negatively affect these resources.

SEP Evaluate Evidence Why is it important to conserve resources and not simply use them in the most convenient way?

....

....

....

....

....

👆 **INTERACTIVITY**

Life of a Landfill

Go online to learn about where to site a landfill and how a landfill is constructed.

Water Pollution

uInvestigate Practice different techniques for cleaning up oil spills.

MS-ESS3-4 Construct an argument supported by evidence for how increases in human population and per-capita consumption of natural resources impact Earth's systems.

Connect It!

 Circle the areas in the photo that contain fresh water.

SEP Provide Evidence Why is water an important resource?

....

....

Water as a Resource

Water is essential for life on Earth. Most of Earth's surface is covered by some form of water, as shown in **Figure 1**. It serves as a habitat for many species. Approximately 97 percent of the water on Earth is undrinkable because it contains salt. Of the remaining 3 percent, most is frozen solid in the polar ice sheets. That leaves less than 1 percent of all the water on the planet as drinkable.

Earth's water is a renewable resource, but fresh water is a limited resource. Recall that water continually moves between the atmosphere and Earth's surface in the water cycle. However, there is not always enough water in a given place at a given time. When water usage is poorly managed, it can lead to water shortages.

The limited supply of fresh water is not evenly **distributed** around the world. Some areas have an abundant supply, while in others it is quite scarce. Water scarcity occurs when there is not enough water to meet demand. It can be caused by droughts, low levels of groundwater, unequal water distribution, or environmental factors such as water pollution. An area faces water scarcity when the water supply is less than 1,000 cubic meters per person.

✓ CHECK POINT **Draw Evidence** Why is water a limited resource even though it is renewable?

....

....

Reflect What do you think the world's freshwater supply will look like in another 100 years? In your science notebook, describe how and why our water supply might change.

Academic Vocabulary

What are some items that might get distributed? Can you think of any examples from your school?

....

....

Fresh Water

Figure 1 In this image of Marsh Lake in Fresno County, California, fresh water may seem abundant. But drinkable fresh water makes up less than one percent of the water on Earth.

Water Pollution

Figure 2 Most sources of freshwater pollution come from human activities.

1. Claim ✏️ Mark any examples of nonpoint sources of pollution with a check mark. Mark any examples of point sources of pollution with an X.

2. Evidence What evidence did you use to identify your claims?

....

....

3. Reasoning Explain how your evidence supports your claim.

....

....

....

....

....

....

....

Sources of Freshwater Pollution

Since fresh water is so limited, any pollution entering the water supply can have drastic short or long-term consequences. Most water pollution is directly linked to human activities, as shown in **Figure 2**. Wastes from farming, households, industry, and mining can end up in the water supply. Water pollutants may be point or nonpoint sources, depending on how they enter the water. A point source for water pollution could be a factory output pipe or a leaking landfill. Nonpoint pollution sources could be farm pesticides, farm animal wastes, or runoff of salt and chemicals from roads.

Farming Wastes Animal wastes, fertilizers, and pesticides are sources of pollution. When it rains, pollutants can run off into nearby water sources and eventually the ocean. Wastes and fertilizers can cause overgrowths of algae. The algae block light and their decomposing remains deplete the water of oxygen, killing everything in the water.

Household Pollutants The water and human wastes that are washed down sinks, showers, and toilets are called **sewage**. Sometimes, the sewage can leak into groundwater before it is treated. Because sewage contains many disease-causing bacteria, people will become ill if they drink or swim in water containing it.

Industrial Wastes The waste products of factories and mines may also pollute the water. Many manufacturing processes use or produce toxic chemicals that need to be disposed of properly. During this disposal, chemicals sometimes leak into the groundwater. Some chemicals, such as heavy metals, build up in the bodies of aquatic organisms, making them and the animals that eat them ill.

Sediment
Erosion carries small particles of rocks and sand from the land into the water. These particles are called **sediment**. Sediment can cover up sources of food, nests, and eggs of aquatic organisms. Sediment also blocks sunlight, which prevents photosynthesis in plants.

Heat
When heat negatively affects bodies of water, it is known as **thermal pollution**. Factories and power plants use water to cool their machinery. This heated water is often discharged back into the environment. Because it is so hot, the water can kill organisms.

Oil and Gasoline
Oil and gasoline are often transported in long pipelines, either underground or above ground. Sometimes these pipelines leak into rivers, streams, or groundwater. When oil and gasoline pollute the water, it can take many years for the ecosystem to recover. Oil is difficult to collect and penetrates much of the soil in the area. It also affects the plants that grow along the water's edge. Spilled oil also has both direct and indirect effects on wildlife. Directly, it coats their fur or feathers and may cause skin irritations. Indirectly, oil may kill their source of food.

Oil and gasoline leaks from underground storage tanks are also sources of water pollution. These leaks can seep into the groundwater, making it unfit to drink.

✓ CHECK POINT **Draw Evidence** Does most water pollution happen as a result of human activities? Explain.

....

....

....

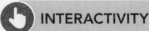 INTERACTIVITY

Examine how pollution affects the water cycle.

Literacy Connection

Draw Evidence Sometimes you need to draw evidence to support your analysis of a certain topic. Reread the previous page and the current page. As you read, underline any pieces of evidence that support the idea that most water pollution is directly linked to human activities.

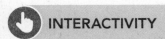 INTERACTIVITY

Investigate whether or not human activity is responsible for odd mutations found in frogs.

Sources of Ocean Pollution

It was once thought that "the solution to pollution is dilution." This meant that whatever was dumped into the ocean would just spread out and eventually go away. Today, we know that isn't true. Dumping large amounts of wastes into the ocean threatens marine organisms and the overall functioning of Earth's systems.

Natural Occurrences There are some "pollutants" that occur naturally. These include unpolluted freshwater runoff from land after heavy rains. When this fresh water enters the ocean, the salinity drops. Some organisms cannot tolerate this, so they either move to saltier waters or die.

Human Activities Most ocean pollution is related to human activities. The chemicals, sewage, and other wastes that are dumped into the ocean come from human sources. Fertilizers and pesticides from farms run off and eventually make it to the ocean. When enough of these build up, they can create an ocean dead zone—an area where nothing can live because there is not enough oxygen in the water.

Trash Trash and plastic, as shown in **Figure 3**, are hazardous to marine animals. For example, sea turtles often mistake plastic bags floating in the water for jellyfish. Once consumed, the bags clog up the intestines of the turtles. Fishing line and nets can catch swimming animals and entangle them. One area in the Pacific Ocean contains about 2 million bits of plastic per square mile. When sea creatures consume these tiny pieces, they can become ill and die. The plastic bits can also cause health problems for animals higher up in the food chain that eat small animals with plastic inside of them.

Effects of Pollution

Figure 3 This plastic and trash was recovered from the ocean, where it can harm organisms.

SEP Design Solutions
What are some ways humans can reduce the amount of plastic that ends up in the ocean?

....

....

....

....

Sources of Oil Pollution

There are different ways for oil to pollute the ocean.

1. Construct Graphs ✏ Create a bar graph of the data.

2. Analyze Proportional Relationships The amount of pollution caused by land runoff is greater than that caused by oil spills. Use ratios to describe how much greater land runoff pollution is than oil spill pollution.

....

Source of Oil Pollution	Oil Pollution (millions of liters)
Offshore drilling	80
Land runoff	1,375
Natural seeps	240
Ship repair	510
Oil spills	125

Oil Spills Oil that is accidentally spilled into the ocean is also a large source of pollution. Oil rigs that drill for oil sometimes leak into the ocean. This oil coats the feathers of birds, reducing their ability to stay warm. Oil also harms animals if they swallow it. Pollutants can build up in organisms' bodies and poison people or other marine life that feed on them.

Aquaculture The practice of raising fish and other water-dwelling organisms for food is called aquaculture. Fish are often raised in artificial ponds and bays that replace and destroy natural habitats, such as salt marshes. The farms can cause pollution and spread diseases into wild fish populations.

 VIDEO

Explore the misconception that the ocean cannot be harmed because it is so vast.

✓ CHECK POINT **Determine Conclusions** How can you help to reduce the amount of pollution that ends up in the ocean?

....

....

....

....

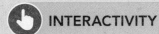
INTERACTIVITY

Take a closer look at water pollution and solutions.

Refugio Oil Spill
Figure 4 In 2015, an oil pipeline off the coast of southern California ruptured. Over 140,000 gallons of crude oil spilled into the ocean and washed up onto the shores of Santa Barbara.

Reducing Water Pollution

Everyone needs clean water. But how can the pollution that currently enters the water be reduced, and what efforts can be made to prevent future pollution?

The United States and other countries have laws that regulate water-polluting substances. These laws mandate the types and amounts of substances that can be dumped into the water. While these laws help, the keys to keeping water clean are the prevention of oil and gasoline spills, effective cleanup of spills, proper sewage treatment, and reduction of pollutants.

Protecting the Ocean The ocean is a continuous body of water. Because no one country owns the ocean, it is every nation's responsibility to do whatever it can to ensure the water stays clean. To help protect the ocean, the United Nations set up regulations that say the first 22 kilometers from the coast are controlled by the nation that owns that coast. That nation also controls any resources, such as oil, natural gas, and fish, that are found out to 370 km.

Many nations are helping to protect the ocean by limiting how much can be taken from it and by establishing marine protected areas (MPAs). They also are working to reduce the amount of pollution in their coastal waters.

Cleaning Oil Spills Oil spills, such as the one in **Figure 4**, are one of the worst environmental hazards that can occur. While nature can clean small amounts of oil from the water, large spills such as the Refugio oil spill are too much to handle. The bacteria that are able to digest oil cannot keep up with the volume of oil that is released in such a spill. Boats deploy skimming devices to collect floating oil, and barriers are set up to absorb or block oil before it reaches the shore. Chemical dispersants are also sprayed into the water to break up the oil. However, oil reached the west coast beaches, including Santa Barbara. Cleanup of a major oil spill in the ocean can take many years.

Improved Farming Methods Modern farming practices reduce water pollution. Formerly, farmers would leave fields bare in winter, allowing soil and fertilizers to wash into streams. It was also common to use large amounts of pesticides, herbicides, and fungicides. These chemicals would run off into streams, polluting the water and killing organisms. Today, farmers can reduce erosion and pollution by leaving stalks in the field or planting winter grasses that hold the soil and nutrients in place. Farmers also treat their land with a smaller amount of chemicals, and find natural predators to combat pests.

Reducing Pollutants Another way to protect Earth's waters is to reduce the amount of pollution that is created. Instead of dumping waste products directly into the environment, manufacturers can recycle them. By turning waste products into new things, the companies may even save money. Another method to reduce waste is to change the way materials are produced. Factories can eliminate the use of non-recyclable materials. By figuring out more environmentally-friendly manufacturing methods, they may make less total waste or less hazardous waste.

You can help to prevent water pollution in your home. Common household water pollutants include paints, paint thinner, motor oil, and garden chemicals. Instead of dumping these into the environment, save these materials for your community's hazardous waste collection day (**Figure 5**), or take them to a specialized facility for such wastes.

Hazardous Waste
Figure 5 Many towns and cities have special recycling centers that provide safe and proper disposal of household chemicals, such as paint and cleaning supplies.

✓ CHECK POINT **Write Explanatory Texts** What can your community do to reduce water pollution?

....

....

....

Plan It !

Reducing Waste in Factories

Many factories are "going green" and changing the way they manufacture products to create less waste. Suppose there is a manufacturing company in your community that is not reducing its waste.

Construct Arguments Come up with a solution to your community's problem. Plan a presentation to convince the factory owners to "go green." How might changing their policy benefit both the community and the factory? How will making these changes impact the environment?

☑ LESSON 4 Check

MS-ESS3-4

1. **SEP Construct Explanations** Why is it so important for sources of fresh water to be protected?

2. **CCC Cause and Effect** How do farming methods cause water pollution?

3. **SEP Provide Evidence** What evidence suggests that factories sometimes cause water pollution?

4. **CCC Analyze Systems** How does water pollution in one area affect water and organisms elsewhere?

5. **Construct Arguments** Write an argument to defend the idea that oil spills are the worst environmental hazard.

Quest CHECK-IN

In this lesson, you learned why fresh water is a limited resource within Earth's systems. You also discovered how human activities lead to water pollution and how humans can reduce freshwater and ocean pollution.

CCC Analyze Systems Why is it important to consider the effects of waste disposal on water sources?

INTERACTIVITY

Reducing Waste

Go online to determine how everyone at your school can work together to reduce wastes and help the environment. Then make a plan to reduce the trash output at your school.

FROM WASTEWATER TO
Tap Water

▶ VIDEO

Walk through the water treatment process.

Fresh water is a precious resource on Earth, so we reuse every drop we can. Wastewater from homes and businesses ends up being recycled for irrigation, manufacturing, and replenishing aquatic ecosystems. But how do you recycle wastewater into drinking water? You engineer it!

The Challenge: To treat wastewater so it can return to the water supply.

Phenomenon In San Diego, California, the Point Loma Wastewater Treatment plant treats wastewater and makes it safe to drink, but it takes several steps. First, water from the sewer system passes through screens that filter out large particles. Next, the water flows into tanks where gravity separates solid waste from the water. Heavy solids sink to the bottom.

The water then flows to a second set of tanks where bacteria digest waste that's still in the water. Then the water is left to settle one more time and the last sediments are removed.

Following that, the water goes through a series of filters to get rid of any small solids or harmful microorganisms. The last step is disinfection using chlorine and UV light. Finally, this water will spend about six months in storage before it arrives at a tap.

DESIGN CHALLENGE

Can you design a model for recycling wastewater or rainwater from your home or school? Go to the Engineering Design Notebook to find out!

A typical wastewater plant has many, many tanks.

Primary Treatment			Secondary Treatment		Disinfection		
Pumping station	Primary screening	Primary sedimentation	Bacteria treatment	Secondary sedimentation	Filtration for micro-organisms	Cleaning with chlorine and UV	Clean water

Wastewater

MS-ESS3-4

Lange's metalmark butterfly

Evidence-Based Assessment

In 1976, ecologists made a disturbing discovery in the Antioch Dunes along the banks of the San Joaquin River in San Francisco, California. A butterfly, formally observed first in 1939 and only found in the dunes, was going extinct. Known as Lange's metalmark butterfly, it became one of the first insects protected as an endangered species by federal law.

Here are some important facts about the butterfly and its habitat:

• Lange's metalmark butterfly produces one crop of offspring each year. Females only lay their eggs on one species of plant, the naked-stem buckwheat plant.

• The dunes where the butterfly lives formed thousands of years ago, when sand deposited by ancient glaciers was moved and shaped by water and wind.

• When the first American settlers arrived in the early 1800s, the dunes ran along the river for about 3 kilometers (2 miles) and reached over 30 meters (100 feet) high in some places.

• As the human population of San Francisco grew, parts of the dunes were leveled and developed for industry. Sand from the dunes was mined to produce bricks and other building materials. The data table shows changes in the human population of San Francisco from 1850 to 2000.

San Francisco County Population, 1850–2000			
Year	Population	Year	Population
1850	21,000	1930	634,394
1860	56,802	1940	634,536
1870	149,473	1950	775,357
1880	233,959	1960	740,316
1890	298,997	1970	715,674
1900	342,782	1980	678,974
1910	416,912	1990	723,959
1920	506,676	2000	776,733

1. **SEP Analyze Data** Which statement about the trends in San Francisco's population growth is valid?
   A. It dropped for a few decades after 1890, but has grown almost every year since then.
   B. It grew slowly each year until 1930, when the population quickly increased.
   C. It increased steadily each decade from the 1850s to the 1950s.
   D. It grew rapidly in the mid to late 1800s and then again in the 1940s.

2. **CCC Cause and Effect** How has mining and extracting sand affected plants that live in the dunes, like the naked-stem buckwheat? Order the events from 1 to 4, with 1 being the first event and 4 being the final event.

Fewer plants like the buckwheat are able to survive due to lack of resources.	———
The population of San Francisco grows dramatically between 1940 and 1950.	———
A lot of sand is removed from the dunes.	———
More pepole require land for roads, homes, and buildings.	———

3. **Apply Scientific Reasoning** The remaining sand dunes became a national wildlife refuge in 1980. A few years later, researchers began an annual count of the butterflies. Between 1999 and 2008, the number of butterflies fell steadily. What might account for this continued drop?

   ....
   ....
   ....
   ....

4. **SEP Engage in Argument** How could an increase in the human population of San Francisco have impacted the Lange's metalmark butterflies that lived there? Use evidence from the text to support your answer.

   ....
   ....
   ....
   ....
   ....
   ....
   ....
   ....
   ....
   ....
   ....
   ....
   ....

Quest FINDINGS

Complete the Quest!

Phenomenon Refine your plan to reduce trash at your school and present the plan.

CCC Cause and Effect We produce a lot of trash that is disposed of in landfills. How would decreasing the trash we generate affect Earth's systems?

....
....
....
....

👆 **INTERACTIVITY**

Reflect on Trash Backlash

MS-ESS3-4

Washing Away

How can you demonstrate the impact of **human activity** on **soil erosion?**

Background

Phenomenon A nearby town is considering a developer's plan to turn riverfront property into shops, restaurants, and apartments. The area is now an undisturbed habitat consisting of trees, bushes, and grasses. Almost all of the natural vegetation will be removed during construction. You will be part of a team tasked with providing an environmental impact report to the town board.

In this lab, you will design and conduct an investigation into the impact of vegetation and ground cover on soil erosion. You will test how quickly water runs off soil in different conditions and how much soil is carried away by the water.

Materials

(per group)

- two 2-liter beverage bottles, cut lengthwise to form troughs
- about 4 cups of potting soil, divided in half
- grass or radish seedlings
- 2 large plastic cups
- 1 liter of water
- watering can with rain spout
- stopwatch

Plan Your Investigation

HANDS-ON LAB

Demonstrate Go online for a downloadable worksheet of this lab.

☐ 1. Work with your partner to design an experimental setup using the materials provided by your teacher. Your experiment must test how fast water runs off the soil and how much soil is carried away in the runoff. As you design your setup, consider the following questions:

- How would you describe the condition of the riverbank before the proposed construction?

- How would you describe the condition of the riverbank during the construction?

- How can you use the materials to model the condition of the riverbank before and during construction?

- How can you design your setup so that you will be able to measure how fast the water runs off the soil and how much soil is contained in the runoff?

- What are your dependent variable and independent variable, and the factors you hold constant?

- How many tests will you run?

- What observations will you make and what data will you collect?

☐ 2. Write a detailed procedure describing how you will investigate the effects of removing vegetation and ground cover on soil erosion. Include any sketches of your setup.

☐ 3. After getting teacher approval for your procedure, conduct your investigation.

☐ 4. Record your observations and data in the table provided.

Procedure and Sketches

Data Table

Bottle	Water Poured (mL)	Water Captured (mL)	Time (sec)	Observations of Water Collected
Grass and soil				
Soil only				

Analyze and Interpret Data

1. **Compare Data** Review the data you collected and the observations you recorded. How do the results of your tests compare?

....

....

....

....

2. **Write an Expression** Suppose you were going to graph the results of your investigation. How would you express the independent variable *Water Poured* as a variable? How would you express the results of your dependent variable *Water Captured* as a variable?

....

....

3. **Apply Scientific Reasoning** Based on the results of your investigation, describe how soil erosion might affect the ecology of rivers, lakes, and other bodies of water.

....

....

....

....

4. **Refine Your Plan** Examine and evaluate the procedures of other teams. Based on what you learned, how might you modify your own procedure to improve the results of your investigation?

....

....

....

....

5. **SEP Engage in Argument** What would you recommend to the town board? Use data from your investigation as evidence to justify your claim.

....

....

....

....

....

MS-ESS3-4, EP&CIIa, EP&CIIb,
EP&CIVb, EP&CVa, EP&CVb

Nothing Goes TO WASTE

One city in Texas is making sure nothing in its sewers goes to waste. The Hornsby Bend Biosolids Management Plant in Austin, Texas, recycles sewage into biosolids. Biosolids are rich in nutrients, so they make great soil and fertilizer.

Every day, Hornsby Bend receives about a million gallons of sewage solids from Austin's water treatment plants, where the sewage is separated from the wastewater. The sewage is screened, and then flows into tanks where bacteria get to work feeding on it. The bacteria break the sewage down, killing most disease organisms as they go. This process is actually not that different from how the human digestive system works. After about 60 days, the sewage is converted into biosolids.

Hornsby Bend also collects Austin's yard trimmings and mixes these with the biosolids to make nutrient-rich soil. The plant sends some soil to nearby farmers who enhance their existing soil with the mix. The rest is used to supplement the soil of Austin's public lawns, gardens, parks, and golf courses. Instead of going to an expensive landfill, the biosolids are put to good use.

Hornsby Bend is also a bird sanctuary with more than 350 types of birds.

All of the water used at the treatment plant is recycled, too. Some of it goes to irrigate the nearby farmland, and the rest goes to ponds at the treatment plant. The nutrient-rich pond water has still another benefit: the treatment plant is also a bird sanctuary. Hornsby Bend is one of the best birding sites in the state. Thanks to the Hornsby Bend Biosolids Management Plant, Austin's waste doesn't go to waste.

Use the table to answer the following questions.

1. **CCC Scale, Proportion, and Quantity** One sample of biosolids contains 18.2 mg/kg mercury, 22.5 mg/kg arsenic, and 29.7 mg/kg cadmium. Are these biosolids safe to use? Why or why not?

   ....

   ....

2. **SEP Use Mathematics** A biosolids plant is picking up waste from a new factory. The level of lead in the plant's biosolids had been 121 mg/kg. With the waste from the new factory, the lead has increased 12 percent. Calculate the new lead level to determine if the biosolid is still safe to use on farmland.

   ....

   ....

   ....

Safe Levels of Pollutants in Soil on Farms Fertilized with Biosolids	
Pollutant	**Risk Assessment Acceptable Soil Concentration (mg/kg-soil)**
Arsenic	23.5
Cadmium	19.7
Copper	769.0
Lead	161.0
Mercury	8.6
Nickel	228.0
Selenium	50.21
Zinc	1,454.0

SOURCE: Environmental Protection Agency

3. **Connect to Society** Why is a chart like this important?

   ....

   ....

   ....

4. **SEP Engage in Argument** Are biosolids safe to use in agriculture? Make an argument to support your answer.

   ....

   ....

   ....

   ....

An EPIC DISASTER

On April 20, 2010, an explosion took place on an oil rig called Deepwater Horizon in the Gulf of Mexico. Within two days the rig had sunk to the ocean floor. Crude oil then leaked from the underwater oil well. The spill lasted 87 days and dumped millions of gallons of oil into the Gulf waters.

Because oil is less dense than water, it floats on the water's surface. The oil in the Gulf disaster, however, did not all float. Scientists estimate that about 10% of it sank to the sea floor. How could a less dense substance sink in a substance of higher density?

Three factors contributed to this phenomenon. First, some oil mixed with natural gas and seawater, causing it to become more dense. The second factor was the climate. Wind currents, ocean waves, and evaporation all acted on the oil and affected its density. The third factor was microorganisms called phytoplankton. They released a sticky substance when exposed to the oil. The substance stuck to bits of algae and other items, causing them to mix with oil and sink.

The Deepwater Horizon oil rig exploded in the Gulf of Mexico on April 20, 2010.

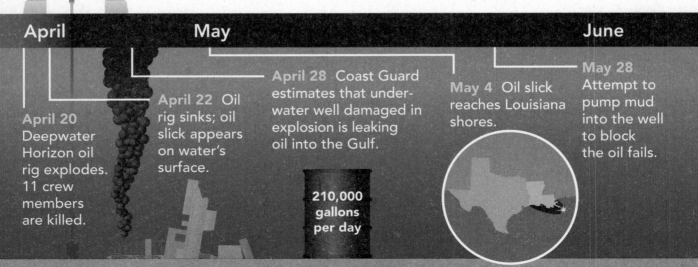

April

May

June

April 20 Deepwater Horizon oil rig explodes. 11 crew members are killed.

April 22 Oil rig sinks; oil slick appears on water's surface.

April 28 Coast Guard estimates that underwater well damaged in explosion is leaking oil into the Gulf.

210,000 gallons per day

May 4 Oil slick reaches Louisiana shores.

May 28 Attempt to pump mud into the well to block the oil fails.

Use the timeline to answer questions 1–2.

1. **SEP Use Mathematics** Approximately how much oil may have spilled into the water between April 20th and July 12th?

....

2. **SEP Construct Explanations** Why do you think it took so long for the workers to stop the flow of oil from the underground well?

....

....

3. **SEP Design Solutions** How might a team of engineers solve the problem of access to an underwater oil well for necessary repairs?

....

....

....

....

4. **Predict** What do you think the nations of the world should do to prevent disasters such as Deepwater Horizon from happening in the future?

....

....

....

July

August

July 5 Oil slick reaches Texas shores.

July 10 Broken containment cap is removed from well; oil now flows without any restrictions.

July 12 New containment cap is installed.

July 15 Oil has ceased to flow from the well.

August 5 The well is permanently sealed.

Take Notes

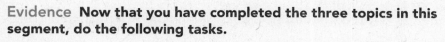

Revisit the Anchoring Phenomenon
Conduct an Investigation

Evidence **Now that you have completed the three topics in this segment, do the following tasks.**

Although many people assume that mining for gold is a thing of the past in California, this is not true. Large- and small-scale mining operations still persist. Some modern miners use a technique called suction dredging to locate gold in California riverbeds. Sediment from riverbeds along with water is mechanically sucked into a machine that separates the gold from the rest of the sediment. The mixture of sediment and water is then pumped back into the river.

Promote Student Discourse 🖊 With a partner, discuss the potential impacts of suction dredging in California.
Work together to complete a concept map to identify some of these impacts. Consider the following questions:

- What are the environmental impacts?

- How is the availability of resources affected?

- How might plants and animals be affected?

- How might humans be affected by these changes?

Impacts of
Suction Dredging

Mining Versus Wildlife

Case Study Suction dredging is a controversial mining method. Some people argue that it damages local ecosystems beyond repair. Miners think differently. You will now play the role of researcher to find out more about suction dredging in California. In particular, you will investigate how suction dredging impacts ecosystems and organisms in California.

Remember, when doing research online, you need to carefully evaluate the websites and information you find. The following suggestions may help you as you conduct your research:

- In the search engine, use phrases that are specific to the subject you are researching, such as *California*, *suction dredging*, *environment*.

- Beware of sites that may be biased or are trying to sell something. Ask yourself, "Why might the author of this website be taking this stance on the topic?"

- Generally, websites that end in *.gov* or *.edu* are more reliable than websites that end in *.com*.

- Take notes as you research and keep a list of the sites you find useful.

A suction dredge uses a motor, so it allows miners to quickly sort through large amounts of sediment.

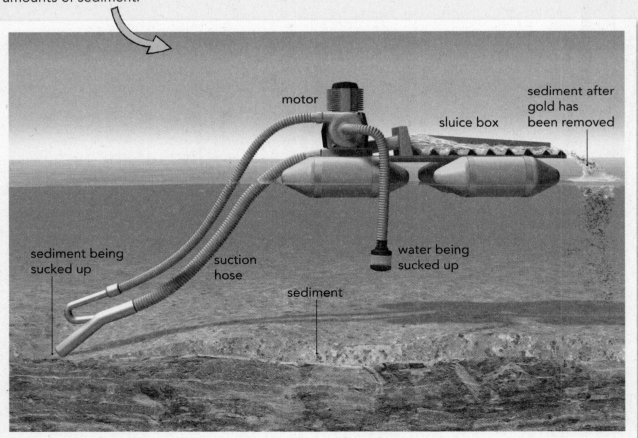

motor

sluice box

sediment after gold has been removed

sediment being sucked up

suction hose

water being sucked up

sediment

Based on your research, answer the following questions.

1. **SEP Construct Explanations** Is suction dredging an issue that everyone across the state in California needs to be concerned with, or do you think the concern is limited to specific areas? Explain.

....

....

....

....

....

2. **CCC Cause and Effect** Which California species are affected by suction dredging? What impact does this mining method have on the availability of resources and the environment?

....

....

....

....

....

....

3. **SEP Engage in Argument** What arguments have the miners made to convince people that they should be allowed to continue mining using this method? Do you think their arguments are valid? Why or why not?

....

....

....

....

....

4. **Connect to Society** What is the current law in California regarding suction dredging? Would you recommend that other states pass similar laws? Why or why not?

....

....

....

APPENDIX A

Safety Symbols

These symbols warn of possible dangers in the laboratory and remind you to work carefully.

 Safety Goggles Wear safety goggles to protect your eyes in any activity involving chemicals, flames or heating, or glassware.

 Lab Apron Wear a laboratory apron to protect your skin and clothing from damage.

 Breakage Handle breakable materials, such as glassware, with care. Do not touch broken glassware.

 Heat-Resistant Gloves Use an oven mitt or other hand protection when handling hot materials, such as hot plates or hot glassware.

 Plastic Gloves Wear disposable plastic gloves when working with harmful chemicals and organisms. Keep your hands away from your face, and dispose of the gloves according to your teacher's instructions.

 Heating Use a clamp or tongs to pick up hot glassware. Do not touch hot objects with your bare hands.

 Flames Before you work with flames, tie back loose hair and clothing. Follow your teacher's instructions about lighting and extinguishing flames.

 No Flames When using flammable materials, make sure there are no flames, sparks, or other exposed heat sources present.

 Corrosive Chemical Avoid getting acid or other corrosive chemicals on your skin or clothing or in your eyes. Do not inhale the vapors. Wash your hands after the activity.

 Poison Do not let any poisonous chemical come into contact with your skin, and do not inhale its vapors. Wash your hands when you are finished with the activity.

 Fumes Work in a well-ventilated area when harmful vapors may be involved. Avoid inhaling vapors directly. Test an odor only when directed to do so by your teacher, and use a wafting motion to direct the vapor toward your nose.

 Sharp Object Scissors, scalpels, knives, needles, pins, and tacks can cut your skin. Always direct a sharp edge or point away from yourself and others.

 Animal Safety Treat live or preserved animals or animal parts with care to avoid harming the animals or yourself. Wash your hands when you are finished with the activity.

 Plant Safety Handle plants only as directed by your teacher. If you are allergic to certain plants, tell your teacher; do not do an activity involving those plants. Avoid touching harmful plants such as poison ivy. Wash your hands when you are finished with the activity.

 Electric Shock To avoid electric shock, never use electrical equipment around water, when the equipment is wet, or when your hands are wet. Be sure cords are untangled and cannot trip anyone. Unplug equipment not in use.

 Physical Safety When an experiment involves physical activity, avoid injuring yourself or others. Alert your teacher if there is any reason you should not participate.

 Disposal Dispose of chemicals and other laboratory materials safely. Follow the instructions from your teacher.

 Hand Washing Wash your hands thoroughly when finished with an activity. Use soap and warm water. Rinse well.

 General Safety Awareness When this symbol appears, follow the instructions provided. When you are asked to develop your own procedure in a lab, have your teacher approve your plan.

GLOSSARY

absolute age The age of a rock given as the number of years since the rock formed.

acid rain Rain or another form of precipitation that is more acidic than normal, caused by the release of molecules of sulfur dioxide and nitrogen oxide into the air.

air mass A huge body of air that has similar temperature, humidity, and air pressure at any given height.

air pressure The pressure caused by the weight of a column of air pushing down on an area.

alluvial fan A wide, sloping deposit of sediment formed where a stream leaves a mountain range.

altitude Elevation above sea level.

amphibian A vertebrate whose body temperature is determined by the temperature of its environment, and that lives its early life in water and its adult life on land.

anticyclone A high-pressure center of dry air.

aquifer An underground layer of rock or sediment that holds water.

asteroid One of the rocky objects revolving around the sun that is too small and numerous to be considered a planet.

astronomical unit A unit of distance equal to the average distance between Earth and the sun, about 150 million kilometers.

atmosphere The relatively thin layer of gases that form Earth's outermost layer.

axis An imaginary line that passes through a planet's center and its north and south poles, about which the planet rotates.

B

biosphere The parts of Earth that contain living organisms.

birth rate The number of people born per 1,000 individuals for a certain period of time.

C

chemical weathering The process that breaks down rock through chemical changes.

climate The average annual conditions of temperature, precipitation, winds, and clouds in an area.

climate change A sudden or gradual change in Earth's climate.

coastline A line that forms the boundary between the land and the ocean or a lake.

comet A loose collection of ice and dust that orbits the sun, typically in a long, narrow orbit.

compression Stress that squeezes rock until it folds or breaks.

condensation The change in state from a gas to a liquid.

conduction The transfer of thermal energy from one particle of matter to another.

conservation The practice of using less of a resource so that it can last longer.

constellation A pattern or grouping of stars that people imagine to represent a figure or object.

continental glacier A glacier that covers much of a continent or large island.

convection The transfer of thermal energy by the movement of a fluid.

convergent boundary A plate boundary where two plates move toward each other.

Coriolis effect The effect of Earth's rotation on the direction of winds and currents.

crust The layer of rock that forms Earth's outer surface.

cryosphere The portion of the hydrosphere that is frozen, including all the ice and snow on land, plus sea and lake ice.

crystal A solid in which the atoms are arranged in a pattern that repeats again and again.

crystallization The process by which atoms are arranged to form a material with a crystal structure.

crystallize To form a crystal structure.

current A large stream of moving water that flows through the oceans.

cyclone A swirling center of low air pressure.

D

death rate The number of deaths per 1,000 individuals in a certain period of time.

deflation The process by which wind removes surface materials.

deforestation The removal of forests to use the land for other reasons.

delta A landform made of sediment that is deposited where a river flows into an ocean or lake.

deposition Process in which sediment is laid down in new locations.

desalination A process that removes salt from sea water to make fresh water.

desertification The advance of desert-like conditions into areas that previously were fertile.

dew point The temperature at which condensation begins.

divergent boundary A plate boundary where two plates move away from each other.

dormant Term used to describe a volcano that is not currently acrtive but able to become active in the future.

drought A long period of low precipitation.

dune A hill of sand piled up by the wind.

E

earthquake The shaking that results from the movement of rock beneath Earth's surface.

eclipse The partial or total blocking of one object in space by another.

El Niño An abnormal climate event that occurs every two to seven years in the Pacific Ocean, causing changes in winds, currents, and weather patterns for one to two years.

ellipse An oval shape, which may be elongated or nearly circular; the shape of the planets' orbits.

emissions Pollutants that are released into the air.

energy The ability to cause change.

equinox Either of the two days of the year on which neither hemisphere is tilted toward or away from the sun.

era One of the three long units of geologic time between the Precambrian and the present.

erosion The process by which water, ice, wind, or gravity moves weathered particles of rock and soil.

evaporation The process by which molecules at the surface of a liquid absorb enough energy to change to a gas.

exponential growth A rate of change that increases more and more rapidly over time.

extinct volcano Term used to describe a volcano that is no longer active and unlikely to erupt again.

F

fault A break in Earth's crust along which rocks move.

flood An overflowing of water in a normally dry area.

flood plain The flat, wide area of land along a river.

fossil The preserved remains or traces of an organism that lived in the past.

fossil fuel Energy-rich substance formed from the remains of organisms.

front The boundary where unlike air masses meet but do not mix.

G

galaxy A huge group of single stars, star systems, star clusters, dust, and gas bound together by gravity.

geocentric Term describing a model of the universe in which Earth is at the center of the revolving planets and stars.

geologic time scale A record of the geologic events and life forms in Earth's history.

geosphere The densest parts of Earth that include the crust, mantle, and core.

glacier Any large mass of ice that moves slowly over land.

global warming A gradual increase in the Earth's average temperature.

gravity The attractive force between objects; the force that moves objects downhill.

greenhouse effect The trapping of heat near a planet's surface by certain gases in the planet's atmosphere.

GLOSSARY

greenhouse gas A gas in Earth's atmosphere that absorbs heat leaving Earth's surface.

groundwater Water that fills the cracks and spaces in underground soil and rock layers.

H

heliocentric Term describing a model of the solar system in which Earth and the other planets revolve around the sun.

hot spot An area where magma from deep within the mantle melts through the crust above it.

humidity A measure of the amount of water vapor in the air.

humus Dark-colored organic material in soil.

hurricane A tropical storm that has winds of about 119 kilometers per hour or higher.

hydrosphere The portion of Earth that consists of water in any of its forms, including oceans, glaciers, rivers, lakes, groundwater and water vapor.

I

ice age Time in Earth's history during which glaciers covered large parts of the surface.

igneous rock A type of rock that forms from the cooling of molten rock at or below the surface.

inertia The tendency of an object to resist a change in motion.

inner core A dense sphere of solid iron and nickel at the center of Earth.

invertebrate An animal without a backbone.

J

jet stream Band of high-speed winds about 10 kilometers above Earth's surface.

L

La Niña A climate event in the eastern Pacific Ocean in which surface waters are colder than normal.

land breeze The flow of air from land to a body of water.

landform A feature on the surface of Earth, such as a coastline, dune, or mountain.

lava Liquid magma that reaches the surface.

law of superposition The geologic principle that states that in horizontal layers of sedimentary rock, each layer is older than the layer above it and younger than the layer below it.

law of universal gravitation The scientific law that states that every object in the universe attracts every other object.

loess A wind-formed deposit made of fine particles of clay and silt.

longshore drift The movement of water and sediment down a beach caused by waves coming in to shore at an angle.

M

magma A molten mixture of rock-forming substances, gases, and water from the mantle.

magnitude The measurement of an earthquake's strength based on seismic waves and movement along faults.

mammal A vertebrate whose body temperature is regulated by its internal heat, and that has skin covered with hair or fur and glands that produce milk to feed its young.

mantle The layer of hot, solid material between Earth's crust and core.

mass extinction When many types of living things become extinct at the same time.

mass movement Any one of several processes by which gravity moves sediment downhill.

mechanical weathering The type of weathering in which rock is physically broken into smaller pieces.

metamorphic rock A type of rock that forms from an existing rock that is changed by heat, pressure, or chemical reactions.

meteor A streak of light in the sky produced by the burning of a meteoroid in Earth's atmosphere.

meteoroid A chunk of rock or dust in space, generally smaller than an asteroid.

meteorologist A scientist who studies the causes of weather and tries to predict it.

mid-ocean ridge An undersea mountain chain where new ocean floor is produced; a divergent plate boundary under the ocean.

mineral A naturally occurring solid that can form by inorganic processes and that has a crystal structure and a definite chemical composition.

moon A natural satellite that orbits a planet.

mountain A landform with high elevation and high relief.

—————— **N** ——————

natural resource Anything naturally occurring in the environment that humans use.

nonpoint source A widely spread source of pollution that is difficult to link to a specific point of origin.

nonrenewable resource A natural resource that is not replaced in a useful time frame.

nuclear fission The splitting of an atom's nucleus into two nuclei, which releases a great deal of energy.

—————— **O** ——————

ocean trench An undersea valley that represents one of the deepest parts of the ocean.

orbit The path of an object as it revolves around another object in space.

ore A mineral deposit large enough and valuable enough for it to be extracted from the ground.

outer core A layer of molten iron and nickel that surrounds the inner core of Earth.

overpopulation A condition in which the number of humans grows beyond what the available resources can support.

ozone A form of oxygen that has three oxygen atoms in each molecule instead of the usual two; toxic to organisms where it forms near Earth's surface.

—————— **P** ——————

penumbra The part of a shadow surrounding the darkest part.

period One of the units of geologic time into which geologists divide eras.

petroleum Liquid fossil fuel; oil.

phase One of the different apparent shapes of the moon as seen from Earth.

planet An object that orbits a star, is large enough to have become rounded by its own gravity, and has cleared the area of its orbit.

plucking The process by which a glacier picks up rocks as it flows over the land.

point source A specific source of pollution that can be identified.

pollution Contamination of Earth's land, water, or air through the release of harmful substances into the environment.

precipitation Any form of water that falls from clouds and reaches Earth's surface as rain, snow, sleet, or hail.

—————— **R** ——————

radiation The transfer of energy by electromagnetic waves.

relative age The age of a rock compared to the ages of other rocks.

relative humidity The percentage of water vapor in the air compared to the maximum amount of water vapor that air can contain at a particular temperature.

renewable resource A resource that is either always available or is naturally replaced in a relatively short time.

reptile A vertebrate whose temperature is determined by the temperature of its environment, that has lungs and scaly skin, and that lays eggs on land.

revolution The movement of an object around another object.

river A natural stream of water that flows into another body of water, such as an ocean, lake, or another river.

rock cycle A series of processes on the surface and inside Earth that slowly changes rocks from one kind to another.

rotation The spinning motion of a planet on its axis.

runoff Water that flows over the ground surface rather than soaking into the ground.

GLOSSARY

sand dune A deposit of wind-blown sand.

satellite An object that orbits a planet.

sea breeze The flow of cooler air from over an ocean or lake toward land.

sea-floor spreading The process by which molten material adds new oceanic crust to the ocean floor.

sediment Small, solid pieces of material that come from rocks or the remains of organisms; earth materials deposited by erosion.

sedimentary rock A type of rock that forms when particles from other rocks or the remains of plants and animals are pressed and cemented together.

seismic wave Vibrations that travel through Earth carrying the energy released during an earthquake.

sewage The water and human wastes that are washed down sinks, toilets, and showers.

shearing Stress that pushes masses of rock in opposite directions, in a sideways movement.

soil The loose, weathered material on Earth's surface in which plants can grow.

solar system The system consisting of the sun and the planets and other objects that revolve around it.

solstice Either of the two days of the year on which the sun reaches its greatest distance north or south of the equator.

star A ball of hot gas, primarily hydrogen and helium, that undergoes nuclear fusion.

storm A violent disturbance in the atmosphere.

storm surge A "dome" of water that sweeps across the coast where a hurricane lands.

stream A channel through which water is continually flowing downhill.

stress A force that acts on rock to change its shape or volume.

subduction The process by which oceanic crust sinks beneath a deep-ocean trench and back into the mantle at a convergent plate boundary.

sun A large, gaseous body at the center of the solar system.

surveying A process in which mapmakers determine distances and elevations using instruments and the principles of geometry.

sustainable Using a resource in ways that maintain it at a certain quality for a certain period of time.

sustainable use The practice of allowing renewable resources time to recover and replenish.

telescope An optical instrument that forms enlarged images of distant objects.

tension Stress that stretches rock so that it becomes thinner in the middle.

thermal energy The total kinetic and potential energy of all the particles of an object.

thermal pollution A type of pollution caused by factories and power plants releasing superheated water into bodies of water.

thunderstorm A small storm often accompanied by heavy precipitation and frequent thunder and lightning.

till The sediments deposited directly by a glacier.

topography The shape of the land determined by elevation, relief, and landforms.

tornado A rapidly whirling, funnel-shaped cloud that reaches down to touch Earth's surface.

transform boundary A plate boundary where two plates move past each other in opposite directions.

transpiration The process by which water is lost through a plant's leaves.

tributary A stream or river that flows into a larger river.

tsunami A giant wave usually caused by an earthquake beneath the ocean floor.

umbra The darkest part of a shadow.

unconformity A gap in the geologic record that shows where rock layers have been lost due to erosion.

uniformitarianism The geologic principle that the same geologic processes that operate today operated in the past to change Earth's surface.

V

valley glacier A long, narrow glacier that forms when snow and ice build up in a mountain valley.

vertebrate An animal with a backbone.

volcano A weak spot in the crust where magma has come to the surface.

W

water cycle The continual movement of water among Earth's atmosphere, oceans, and land surface through evaporation, condensation, and precipitation.

watershed The land area that supplies water to a river system.

well A hole sunk into the ground to reach a supply of water.

wind The horizontal movement of air from an area of high pressure to an area of lower pressure.

INDEX

Page numbers in Bold are vocabulary terms. Italic page numbers are of charts, graphs, pictures, and features.

A IS4

Academic Vocabulary. *See* Vocabulary, Academic
Accidental synthetics, *85*
Active volcano, 50
African Plate, *27*
Agriculture
    impact of, *105*
    land and, 120
    soil management and, 121–124
    water pollution and, 132, 137
Air pollution
    acid rain, *112*
    causes of, *109–110*
    controlling, 114–115
    death, causing, 114
    emissions and, 110, 114
    indoor, 113
    outdoor, 110–112
    ozone layer and, 115
    smog, 111
    types of, 109
Allergens, 113
Amplitude (seismic waves), 38
Anchoring Phenomenon, 1
Anthracite, 65
Anticlines, 36, *36*
Application of Skills. *See* **Connect It!; Design It!; Math Toolbox; Model It!; Question It!; uDemonstrate Lab; uEngineer It!**
Aquaculture, 135
Aquifers, 85
Assessment, Evidence-Based Assessment, 54–55, 90–91, 140–141
    Lesson Check, 20, 31, 42, 53, 72, 81, 88, 107, 116, 129, 138
Asthenosphere, *46*
Atlantic Ocean, 19
Automobiles, 114

B IS4

Bedrock, *121*
Before the Topic, Identify the Problem, 2–6
Benitoite, 80
Bike sharing, *114*
Birth rate, **102**

Bitumen, 65
Boundaries (plate tectonics), 27–30
    faults and, 34
    volcanos and, 45–46
Brown, Governor Jerry, 117
Butterflies, *140*

C IS4

Calderas, 49
California
    air pollution and, 114, 117
    chain island, *9*
    climate change and, 117
    Death Valley, *34*
    droughts in, 86, 89, *113*
    geology of, *28, 30, 34, 36*
    Imperial Valley, *28*
    Inyo craters, 84
    Loma Prieta earthquake, *33*
    Los Angeles population, 101
    Management Act, 89
    minerals and rocks, 78, 80
    Oakland, *33*
    oil spills, 66
    Palmdale, *36*
    Salton Sea, *28*
    Salton Trough, *28*
    San Andreas Fault, 30, 34
    Sustainable Groundwater
    tsunamis, *43*
    wind farms in, 119
California Spotlight
Before the Topics, Identify the Problem, 2–6
Revisit the Anchoring Phenomenon
    Communicate a Solution, 153
    Conduct an Investigation, 151–152
Case Studies
    Nothing Goes to Waste, 124–147
    An Epic Disaster, 148–149
Cascade Mount Range, California, *10–11*
Carbon dioxide, 110
Carbon monoxide, 113
Check Point
    analyze text, 77
    cite evidence, 63
    cite textual evidence, 17, 19, 30, 41, 52, 68, 111, 120

    determine central ideas, 34, 64, 109
    determine conclusions, 47, 71, 103, 105, 115, 135
    determine meaning, 78
    develop an argument, 106
    draw conclusions, 25
    draw evidence, 124, 128, 131, 133
    identify, 87
    integrate with visuals, 27, 113, 125
    summarize, 85
    summarize text, 15, 36, 80
    translate Information, 123
    write arguments, 112
    write explanatory texts, 137
Cinder cone volcanos, 49
Clear-cutting, *120*
Climate
    as evidence for plate tectonics, 15
Climate change, 117
Coal, 64–65
Composite volcanos, 48, **48**, *48*
Compression (plate tectonics), **33**
Connect It!
    Apply Scientific Reasoning, 100
    Cause and Effect, 32, 118
    Classify, 62
    Construct Explanations, 74, 108
    Make Predictions, 108
    Provide Evidence, 130
    Stability and Change, 12, 22
    Systems, 44, 82
Connect to Nature of Science, 31
Connect to You, 21, 73
Conservation, **106**
Constraints, 104
Continental crust, *46*
    plate tectonics and, 24, *24*
Continental drift, 13–15, *13, 14,* 21
    See also **Plate tectonics**
Convection, plate tectonics and, 24, *24*
Convergent boundaries, **27**, 29, *29,* 30, 34, 46
Crosscutting Concepts (CCC)
    Cause and Effect, 3, 20, 31, 32, 40, 55, 68, 72, 77, 81, 86, 88, 91, 95, 105, 107, 116, 118, 121, 122, 129, 138, 141, 153
    Patterns, 53, 69, 81, 91

Scale, Proportion, and Quantity, 39, 147

Stability and Change, 12, 19, 22, 42, 59

Structure and Function, 53

Systems and System Models, 17, 18, 44, 65, 67, 69, 79, 82, 85, 95

Crust (Earth), plate tectonics and, *24*

Crust (Earth), plate tectonics and, 24

Crystallization, **77**

D IS4

Death rate, **102**

Death Valley, *34*

Deforestation, **120**

Desalination, **87**

Desertification, *123*

Design It! 87

Development, of land, *120*

Distribution, 131

Divergent boundaries, **27**, 28, *30*, 34, 46

Dormant volcanos, **50**

Droughts, *123*

E IS4

Earthquakes, 27, 37–40, **37**
damage from, *33*
Loma Prieta earthquake, 33
risk map, *40*
tsunamis and, 40–41

Earth's layers
convection currents and, 24, *24*
crust, 33–36
plate tectonics and, 33–36

East African Rift System, 46

Emissions, **110**, 114

Energy
alternative sources of, 114
consumption of, *104*
see also **Photosynthesis**

Energy sources. See **Natural resources**

Engineering
Defining the Problem, 73
Impact on Society, 139
Sustainable Design, 43, 73

See also **Science and Engineering Practices; uEngineer It!**

Environment, human impacts on. see **Human impacts on the environment**

Environment. See **Ecosystems; Habitats**

Environmental issues. See **Ecological issues**

Environmental Principles and Concepts, 8, 44, 60

Epicenter, 37–39, *38, 39*

Erosion, *122*, 123, 142–145

Eruptions, quiet and explosive, 50–51

Estimate, *142*

Eurasian Plate, 25, *25, 27, 29*

Evidence-Based Assessment, 54–55, 90–91, 140–141

Exponential growth, **103**

Extinct volcano, **50**

F IS4

Farming methods, 137

Farming wastes, 132

Fault-block mountains, 35, *35*

Faults (plate tectonics), **34**, *34*
new landforms, 35–36

Features. See **California Spotlight; Careers; Case Studies; Global to Local; Extraordinary Science; It's All Connected; uDemonstrate Lab; uEngineer It!**

Fertilizers, 122

Folding (plate tectonics), 35–36, *36*

Footwalls, 34, *34*

Forest fires, 110

Fossil fuels, 64, 119
coal, 64–65
natural gas, 68
oil, 66–67
usage issues, 70

Fossils and plate tectonics, 14

Fracking, 68

Freshwater pollution, *132–133*

G IS4

Gasoline, 133

Geosphere. *see* **Minerals**

Global to Local, 117

Gold mining,
Gold Rush, 2–6, 78

Greenhouse gases, 117

Groundwater, 83, 85

H IS4

Hanging walls, 34, *34*

Hawaiian Islands volcanic activity, 47, 50

Hazardous waste, *137*

Heat transfer, thermal pollution, 133

Himalayan mountains, *23, 29, 29*

Hot spot volcanism, **47**, *47*

Household pollutants, 132

Human impacts on the environment
air pollution, 108–115
impacts on land, 118–128, 142–145
population growth, 101–103
resource consumption, 104–106
water pollution, 130–137

Human population
changes in, 102
growth of, 101, *102, 107*
growth rate of, 103
overpopulation, 105
San Francisco county population, 140

Hydrocarbons, 68, 111

Hydroelectric power, 73

I IS4

Iceland, 28

Imperial Valley, California, *28*

Indian-Australian Plate, *27, 29*

Indoor air pollution, *113*

Indoor gases, 113

Industrial Revolution, 102

Industrial wastes, 132

Inquiry Skills. See **Science and Engineering Practices**

Intergovernmental Working Group for the Climate Action Team, 117

INDEX

Page numbers in Bold are vocabulary terms. Italic page numbers are of charts, graphs, pictures, and features.

Investigative Phenomenon
Human Impacts on the Environment, 96
past plate motion, 8
Distribution of Natural Resources, 60–61
uneven natural resource distribution, 60

It's All Connected
Managing California's Water Resources, 89
The Slow Acceptance of Continental Drift, 21

K IS4

Kilauea volcano, 110
Krakatau volcano, 51

L IS4

Labs
Hands-On Labs, 20, 23, 53
uConnect, 8, 61, 97
uDemonstrate
To Drill or Not to Drill, 92–95
Modeling Sea-Floor Spiral, 56–57
Washing Away, 142–145
uInvestigate, 12, 15, 22, 29, 32, 37, 44, 46, 74, 75, 82, 85, 100, 104, 108, 110, 118, 120, 130, 136
Lakes, 84
Land
agriculture and, 120
degradation of, 123
development of, 120
mining and, 120
as resource, 119
soil management, 111–114, 132–135
uses of, *120*
Land reclamation, *124*
Landfills, 124
Landforms
plate tectonics and, 14, 35–36
volcanic, 48–49
Landslides, 41
Lange's metalmark butterfly, *140*
Lava, 44–53, *45*, 48, 77
Lava plateaus, 49

Lignite, 65
Literacy Connection
Cite Textual Evidence, 14, 69, 112, 125
Determine Conclusions, 105
Determine Meaning, 76
Draw Evidence, 133
Evaluate Media, 40
Integrate with Visuals, 27, 48
Support Author's Claim, 86
Lithosphere, 46
Litter, *121*
Logging, *106*
Loma Prieta earthquake, *33*
Los Angeles, *101*

M IS4

Magma, 44–53, **45**, 77
formation of, 48
types of, 51
Magma chamber, 48–52
Magnitude, 39, *39*
Mantle (Earth)
movement in, 24–25, *24*
sea-floor spreading, *17, 18*
Mapping, of ocean ridges, *16*
Marine protected areas (MPAs), 136
Math Connection
Analyze Graphs, 39,
Analyze Proportional Relationships, 51
Analyze Relationships, 68, 114, 123, 135
Construct Graphs, 135
Draw Comparative Inferences, 84
Evaluate Evidence, 103
Interpret Data, 103
Reason Quantitatively, 28
use ratio reasoning, 114
Math Toolbox
Causes of Land Degradation, 123
Distribution of Water Resources, 84
Energy Usage, 114
Finding an Epicenter, 39
Magma Composition, 51
Natural Gas Consumption in the U.S., 68
Projected Growth Rates, 103

Rates of Plate Movement, 28
Sources of Oil Pollution, 135
Matter, cycles of. *see* Cycles of matter
Measuring
magnitude of earthquakes, 39
Micro-hydro power, 73
Mid-ocean ridges, 16, *16, 17, 18,* 28, 46
Minerals
distribution, 78–79
formation, 76–77
use, 80
Mineral resources, 73–81
Mining, 80, *120*
Model It! 19, 26, 38, 47, 115
Moment magnitude graph, *39*
Mount Everest, 23, 29, *29*
Mount Kilauea volcano, 50
Mount Rainier, California, *10–11*
Mountain ranges
as evidence for plate tectonics, 23, *23*
folding and, 35–36
formation of, 27, 29, 35–36

N IS4

Natural gas, 68
Natural resources
balancing needs, 106
defined, **63, 119**
human activities and, 104
impact on Earth system, 105
mineral resources, 73–81
nonrenewable, 63–72, *119*
renewable, *119*
water resources, 82–88
see also **Ecological issues**
Nitrogen oxides, 111, 112
Nonpoint source, 109
Nonrenewable resources, 63–72, ***119***
fossil fuels, 64–68
nuclear power, 69
Normal faults, 34, *34*
North American Plate, 25, *25, 27*
North American, predicting movement of, *19*
Nuclear fission, 69
Nutrient depletion, 122

O IS4

Oakland, California, *33*
Oceans
    and natural resources, 87
    and pollution, 87
Ocean floor uplift, 40–41
Ocean ridges, 16–19, *19*
Ocean trenches, 18–19, **18**, *18,
    19*, 27, 46
Oceanic crust, 24, *24*, 46
Oceans
    earthquakes in, 40–41
    plate tectonics and, 16–19, 27
    pollution of, 134–135
    protection of, 136
    sea-floor spreading, *17*
Oil
    water pollution and, 66–67, 133,
    135
Ore, 75
Overpopulation, 105
Ozone, 111, *115*

P IS4

P waves, 37–39, *37, 39*
Pacific Ocean, 19
Pacific Plate, *27, 47*
Palmdale, California, *36*
Pangaea, 13–15, 25, *25*
Peat, 65
Petroleum, 66–67
Phenomenon
    anchoring phenomenon, 1
    oil drilling, 92
    past plate motion, 8
    sea-floor spreading, 56
    tsunamis, 43
Plan It!, 70, 121, 137
Plate boundaries, 27–30, *27*
    volcanos and, 45–46
Plastics, 134
Plate tectonics, 8–59
    earthquakes and tsunamis and,
    26, *26*, 27, 37–40
    earth's crust and, 33–36
    earth's surface and, 12–31
    evidence of, 12–20
    faults, 34
    plate boundaries and, 27–30,
    45–46
    theory of, 22–27

volcanos and, 26, *26*, 45–47
**Point Loma Wastewater
    Treatment plant,** 139
Point source, 109
Pollution, 105
    air pollution, 109–115
    and fossil fuels, 64–68, 70
    defined, 109
    of water, 86
    thermal pollution, 133
    water pollution, 130–137
    see also **Ecological issues**
Population. *see* **Human
    population**
Primary, 111
Process Skills. *See* **Science and
    Engineering Practices**
Project-Based Learning. *See*
    Quest

Q IS4

Quest Check-In
    Life of a Landfill, 129
    Monitoring a Volcano, 42
    More Trash, Less Space, 107
    Mount Rainer's Threat, 31
    Patterns in the Cascade range,
    20
    Reducing Waste, 138
    Signs of Eruption?, 53
    Trash vs. Water, 116
Quest Check-In Labs, 20, 31, 42,
    53, 107, 116, 129, 138
Quest Findings, 55, 91, 99, 141
Quest Kickoff, 98
Quest PBL
    To Hike or Not to Hike, 10–11
    Reduce Your School's Impact on
    Earth Systems, 98–99
Question It! 52, 78, 104

R IS4

Radon, 113
Ratios, 107
Reading and Literacy Skills
    Cause and Effect, 32
    Cite Textual Evidence, 14, 17,
    19, 30, 41, 52
    Compare and Contrast, 31, 49
    Determine Central Ideas, 34,
    38

    Determine Conclusions, 47
    Draw Conclusions, 25
    Evaluate Media, 40
    Evidence, 6, 26
    Infer, 20
    Integrate with Visuals, 14, 16,
    24, 25, 27, 47, 48
Recycling, 137
Refugio Oil Spill, 136
Renewable resources, *119*
Reverse faults (plate tectonics),
    34, *34*
Rift valleys, 28, 35, *35*
Ring of Fire, 26, *26*, 40, *40*
Rivers, 84
Rocks
    as evidence of plate tectonics,
    17
    from ocean floor, 17, *17*
Rocky Mountains, 34

S IS4

S waves, 37–39, *37, 39*
Salton Sea, California, *28*
Salton Trough, California, *28*
San Andreas Fault, California, 30,
    34
San Francisco county population,
    140
Santa Barbara, California, 136
**Science and Engineering
    Practices (SEP)**
    Analyzing and Interpreting
    Data, 20, 31, 38, 39, 53, 55, 59,
    66, 77, 91, 103, 141
    Asking Questions and Defining
    Problems, 42, 104
    Constructing Explanations and
    Designing Solutions, 31, 42, 46,
    51, 53, 55, 59, 65, 72, 74, 81,
    84, 87, 88, 91, 95, 108, 138
    Developing and Using Models,
    17, 34, 37, 48, 49, 55, 57, 59,
    65, 69, 85, 95, 115
    Engaging in Argument from
    Evidence, 26, 28, 42, 55, 67, 72,
    107, 116, 130, 141, 145
    Obtaining, Evaluating, and
    Communicating Information, 20,
    36, 52, 103, 116
    Planning and Carrying Out
    Investigations, 70
    Using Mathematics and
    Computational Data, 28, 51,
    66, 68

INDEX

Page numbers in Bold are vocabulary terms. Italic page numbers are of charts, graphs, pictures, and features.

Science Notebook
Make Meaning, 33
Reflect, 15
Sea-floor spreading, 17
Seamounts, 29, 47
Seas. *See* Oceans
Sea turtles, 134
Sediment, 133
Seismic waves, measuring,
38–39, *38*
Seismographs, 38–39, *38*
Sewage, 132
Shield volcanos, *49*
Skills. *See* Reading and
Literacy Skills; Science and
Engineering Practices (SEP)
Smog, 111
Soil management
desertification, 123
erosion, *122*, 142–145
land reclamation, 124
landfills, 124
nutrient depletion, 122
structure of soil, *121*
wetlands, *125*
South American Plate, *27*
South Lake Reservoir, *123*
Spectrometer, *52*
Stress (plate tectonics), 33
Strike-slip faults, 34, *34*
Strip mining, *120*
Subduction, 18–19, **18,** 29
volcanos and, 46, *46*
Subsoil, *121*
Suess, Edward, 14
Sulfur dioxides, 112
Surface water, 83–84
Sustainable, 126
Sustainable use, 106
Synclines, 36, *36*

T IS4

Tectonic plates. *See* Plate
tectonics
Temperature inversion, *111*
Tension (plate tectonics), 33, 35
The Origins of Continents and
Oceans, 13
Thermal pollution, 133
Timber, *106*
Toolbox, Math Toolbox, 28, 39, 51

Tools
seismographs, 38–39
spectrometer, *52*
tiltmeters, 52
Topsoil, *121*
Transform boundaries, 27, 30, *30*
Triangulation, 38
Tsunamis, 27, 40–41, **41,** *41,* 43,
43

U IS4

uConnect Lab, 8, 61, 97
uDemonstrate Lab
To Drill or Not to Drill, 92–95
Modeling Sea-Floor Spreading,
56–59
Washing Away, 142–145
uEngineer It!
Designing to Prevent
Destruction, 43
From Wastewater to Tap Water,
139
Micro-Hydro Power, 73
uInvestigate Labs, 12, 15, 20, 22,
29, 32, 37, 44, 46, 53, 74, 75,
82, 85, 100, 104, 108, 110, 118,
120, 130, 136
Uranium, 69

V IS4

Vocabulary, Academic, 13, 23,
35, 48, 50
Volcanic eruptions, 110
Volcanic island arcs, 46, *46*
Volcanic islands, 28–29, 46, *46*
Volcanism, *45*
Volcanos, 44–53, **45**
extinct, dormant, and active, 50
formation and structures, 48–49
hazards, 50–52
plate tectonics and, 18, 27
volcanism, *45*

W IS4

Waste
agricultural, 132
hazardous, 137
impact on environment, 105
industrial, 132

landfills and, 124
reducing, 137
wastewater recycling, 139
water pollution and, 132
Water
fresh water, *131*
as a resource, 131
scarcity of, 104, 131
wastewater recycling, 139
wetlands, *125*
Water pollution
effects of, *134*
farming methods and, 137
reducing, 136–137
sources of freshwater pollution,
132–133
sources of ocean pollution,
134–135
Water resources, 82–88, *89*
and desalination, 87
distribution of, 83–85, *89*
groundwater, 83, 85
human impact on, 86–87
oceans, 87
surface water, 83–84
Waves, seismic, 37–39, *37*
Wegener, Alfred, 13–15, 21, *21*
Wegener's hypothesis, 13–15, 21
Wells, 85
Windfarms, *119*
World politics, and fossil fuels,
70
Writing Skills
cite textual evidence, 14, 17,
19, 30, 41, 52
summarize text, 15, 36
See also Science Notebook

Y IS4

Yellowstone National Park, 47

CREDITS

Photography

Photo locators denoted as follows: Top (T), Center (C), Bottom (B), Left (L), Right (R), Background (Bkgrd)

Covers

Front: Tufa Formations, Art Wolfe/Stone/Getty Images; Back: Marinello/DigitalVision Vectors/Getty Images

Instructional Segment 4

iv: Nick Lundgren/Shutterstock; vi: Gary Crabbe/AGE Fotostock; vii: Jeff J Daly/Alamy Stock Photo; viii: KPG Payless2/Shutterstock; xBkgrd: Brian J. Skerry/National Geographic/Getty Images; xT: Fabriziobalconi/Fotolia; xiB: Dale Kolke/ZUMA Press/Newscom; 001: Andrew J. Russell/Everett Collection Historical/Alamy Stock Photo; 002: TopFoto/The Image Works; 003: Marcel Clemens/Shutterstock; 004BL: Don Bendickson/AGE Fotostock; 004BR: History Images/Alamy Stock Photo; 005: Andrew J. Russell Everett Collection Historical/Alamy Stock Photo; 008: Gary Crabbe/AGE Fotostock; 010: Christopher Boswell/Shutterstock; 017L: Mr. Elliot Lim and Mr. Jesse Varner, CIRES & NOAA/NCEI; 017R: OAR/National Undersea Research Program/NOAA; 021: Sueddeutsche Zeitung Photo/Alamy Stock Photo; 022: MarkushaBLR/Fotolia; 028: Ed Burns/EyeEm/Getty Images; 029T: David Burton/Alamy Stock Photo; 029B: Vadim Petrakov/Shutterstock; 034: Bill Perry/Fotolia; 036: Tom Uhlman/Alamy Stock Photo; 041: JIJI PRESS/AFP/Getty Images; 043: Nat Farbman/ The LIFE Images Collection/Getty Images; 044: Pall Gudonsson/Getty Images; 050L: Siim Sepp/Alamy Stock Photo; 050R: Sandatlas/Shutterstock; 051: Hulton Archive/Getty Images; 052T: Janet Babb/Hawaiian Volcano Observatory/U.S. Geological Survey; 052B: Rosa Irene Betancourt 3/Alamy Stock Photo; 057: Space_Expert/Fotolia; 060: Jeff J Daly/Alamy Stock Photo; 062: Chon Kit Leong/Alamy Stock Photo; 064: Aleksandr Pobedimskiy/Shutterstock; 066: Louisiana Governor's Office/Alamy Stock Photo; 068: Matt Gentry/The Roanoke Times/AP Images; 071: Everett Historical/Shutterstock; 074: Henryk Sadura/Shutterstock; 076: WaterFrame/Alamy Stock Photo; 077T: Shu-Hung Liu/Shutterstock; 077B: Siim Sepp/Alamy Stock Photo; 078: SuperStock/Alamy Stock Photo; 080: The Natural History Museum/Alamy Stock Photo; 084: David McNew/Newsmakers/Hulton Archive/Getty Images; 087: Bennyartist/Shutterstock; 089: Justin Sullivan/Getty Images; 092: Haizhen Du/Shutterstock; 093T: iStock/Getty Images; 093B: Anton Starikov/Alamy Stock Photo; 096: KPG Payless2/Shutterstock; 098: National Geographic Creative/Alamy Stock Photo; 100: Justin Lambert/Getty Images; 105: Design Pics Inc/Alamy Stock Photo; 106: Kletr/Shutterstock; 108: Por Nahorski Pavel/Shutterstock; 112: Karol Kozlowski/Shutterstock; 114: Mark Kauzlarich/Bloomberg/Getty Images; 115: Science Source; 117: Chieko Hara/The Porterville Recorder/AP Images; 118: Jade Brookbank/Getty Images; 120TL: Chad Ehlers/Alamy Stock Photo; 120TR: Jiri Foltyn/Shutterstock; 120B: Rob Crandall/Alamy Stock Photo; 121: Perytskyy/iStock/Getty Images; 122L: Kletr/Shutterstock; 122R: Blickwinkel/Alamy Stock Photo; 123: Tom Grundy/Alamy Stock Photo; 124: FL Historical/Alamy Stock Photo; 126: Lowsun/Shutterstock; 128: Tom McHugh/Science Source; 130: iStock/Getty Images; 134: Rosanne Tackaberry/Alamy Stock Photo; 136: David McNew/Getty Images; 137: ZUMA Press Inc/Alamy Stock Photo; 140: Al Donner/USFWS; 142: Philipp Dase/Shutterstock; 146: Philip Duff/Alamy Stock Photo; 148: U.S. Coast Guard Photo.

Take Notes

Use this space for recording notes and sketching out ideas.

Take Notes

Use this space for recording notes and sketching out ideas.

Take Notes

Use this space for recording notes and sketching out ideas.

Use this space for recording notes and sketching out ideas.

Take Notes

Use this space for recording notes and sketching out ideas.

Take Notes